Introduction

This reprint of Volume Five, eight years after its first printing, now has another great collection illustrated. The Taradash collection written by Albert and Donald Sack. It gives a moving history, of the time 1934 thru 1980, of the forming of this great collection, which is now passing to another generation of collectors.

The Taradash collection starts on page 1115 and continues throughout Volume Five. This was done so that the first printing and second printing would have the same index of pages and items.

Volume Five now contains three great collections. The Robb collection, The Davis collection and Taradash collection. It contains over twenty-four hundred objects, most of them illustrated for the first time with forty-eight pages of furniture masterpieces in full color.

The scholarship that has gone into authenticating the pieces these volumes contain and the subsequent value to collectors and students of Americana insure they are well worth the investment.

The index has been arranged in five ways:

First — Form: Items listed alphabetically and also listed in periods,
        Example: Chairs — Pilgrim, William and Mary, etc.

Second — Regional: Items listed by location.
        Example: New York — Bureaus, Chairs, etc.
        Also large states such as Massachusetts
        have centers within them listed
        separately.

Third — Cabinetmakers: Listed in alphabetical order.

Fourth — Clockmakers: Listed in alphabetical order.

Fifth — Silversmiths and Painters: Listed in alphabetical order.

Each item is listed by p. for page number and item number following the page number in the catalog. Example p. 100, 68. Also in the index, where the craftsman is now, the name is preceded by page number and item number. This index is extremely valuable in locating the item one is researching.

This set of volumes covers the endless variety and range existent in the field of Americana, which suffers from the lack of adequate indexed, printed and illustrative material necessary for collectors and students of Americana. I know that you will find these volumes a source of pleasure and a valuable tool for research and reference, as I have.

I commend them to you.

Joseph Hennage

Joseph H. Hennage
Highland House Publisher

Albert Sack

Donald Sack

I want to personally thank Albert and Donald Sack for the Taradash documentation. They spent many hours researching and gathering the photographs. It is a documentation I know you will enjoy.

Joseph H. Hennage
Highland House Publisher Inc.

A SAGA OF CONNOISSEURSHIP
THE TARADASH COLLECTION

Mr. and Mrs. Mitchel Taradash and son, Michael.

1934 was a very bad year in the annals of the nation and the fortunes of Israel Sack. The Great Depression had wreaked its havoc for over four years, and its effect on antiques and every form of business had been devastating. Israel Sack had already established a national reputation as the Dean of American antique dealers during his career in Boston, and he was not one to be stopped by a mere depression. This was the man who almost single handedly was responsible for the creation of American sections in the Mid-western museums, in the William Rockhill Nelson Galleries, in Kansas City, the City Art Museum of St. Louis, and the Detroit Art Institute, who furnished the Wayside Inn for Henry Ford and whose career and association with Henry Ford is recorded in the permanent archives of the history of the Ford Motor Company, who sold many masterpieces to Henry du Pont which formed an important part of the collection at Winterthur. He bought

continued on page 1129

Pilgrim early maple Hadley chest, initialed KK, Massachusetts circa 1680-1700. Illustrated "The Hadley Chest" Luther No. 44. Ex-collection Mrs. S. R. Bertron, Oyster Bay, L.I., New York. Private collection.

"Great" armchair by John Gaines, Portsmouth, New Hampshire, circa 1724-1735. Illustrated "Fine Points of Furniture, Early American" page 19. Private collection.

P4214 Pennsylvania German Open dresser, made of long leaf pine and retaining the original blue green decoration; the panelled doors of the base have painted flower pots with tulips and daisies and the date "ANNO 1787." The sides of the upper case are finely scalloped while the scalloping of the crest board complements that of the base. Pennsylvania circa 1787. To our knowledge this is the only scalloped dresser with Pennsylvania German decoration.
Ex-collection Mr. and Mrs. Mitchel Taradash.
Illustrated "LIVING WITH ANTIQUES" Winchester, page 90.

Ht. 83″ Lg. 62″ Dp. 18″

THE S S CHEST, NO. 81

Pilgrim oak "Hadley" chest with one drawer and bearing the initials SS for Sarah Smith, daughter of Deacon John Smith of Hadley, Massachusetts, made in Hadley, Massachusetts, circa 1700-1710. This piece is in the finest original state with a dark brown patina of great character. The bale handles are later additions.

This chest is illustrated in "The Hadley Chest" by Luther, page 112. The page from Luther's book tracing the chest's fascinating career is here reproduced. The chest was purchased by us from the Sweet family.

P4122 Queen Anne mahogany blockfront kneehole desk of rare small size, the center recessed compartment is removable, the brass H-hinges for the arched panelled door are original as are the bat wing brasses; the center pullout drawer has diamond and scroll motifs. Salem, Massachusetts, circa 1735-1750. The desk descended in the Metcalf family. Miniatures of Eliah Wight Metcalf and Lydia Stedman Metcalf accompany the piece.

Ht. 31½″ Wd. 33¾″ Dp. 20¾″

P4029 Mahogany fire screen with gilt decoration, Chippendale in form with Federal influence; tripod base with finely sculptured claw and ball feet, C-scrolled borders, rosette and leaf carved knees; the spiral column is supported on a fluted urn, the fluted urn design and spiral repeated on the flame finial which has a gilt beaded base; the original large oval screen has a moulded frame with gilt beaded inner border enclosing a beautifully preserved silkwork embroidery—a cluster of flowers tied with a bowknot with an outer floral border in brilliant colors; original finish and gilding; Salem, Massachusetts, circa 1790-1810.

This fire screen descended in the family of Elias Haskett Derby of Salem and was obtained from direct descendants.

Ht. 61″ Screen 21½″ x 23″

Comparison of this screen with other Derby masterpieces in the Museum of Fine Arts, Boston, is rewarding.

1. The magnificent screen illustrated in Randall "American Furniture" plates 114 and A. The cabriole, the precision sculpture of the ball and claw feet and the C-scrolled borders suggest the same hand. Another interesting relationship is in the pattern of the embroidery, the bowknot in this example holding the cluster while in the Museum's example the basket suspends from a similar bowknot. The floral borders of both screens are also similar.

2. The superb dressing glass illustrated Hipkiss "M. & M. Karolik Collection" plate 136. The rosettes that border the glass and from which the drapery supports suspend are the same as the rosettes on the knees of this screen.

The form and carvings of this screen are more understated and less Classical in their expression, suggesting the theory that it slightly predates the richer McIntire example and served as the inspiration for Elias Haskett Derby or Elizabeth Derby to emulate on a more ambitious scale.

P3753 Chippendale mahogany block and shell carved bureau with raised dished top, the finely modelled domed shells have broad fluted centers in scrolled borders, ogee bracket feet with marginal carved inner borders, Connecticut probably Middletown circa 1760-1780.

The piece is in untouched original condition including the finish and the beautiful chased bale brasses.

Ht. 36″ Wd. 38½″ Dp. 19″

P2270 Chippendale cherry block and shell chest-on-chest with claw and ball feet; wavy scrolled apron, concave blocked and fan carved center panel in upper case, fluted columns with Corinthian capitals; original carved flame finials and brasses. Norwich, Connecticut, circa 1770-1790. Descended in the Trumbull family of Norwich. Illustrated Nutting FURNITURE TREASURY, Volume I, #323; Lockwood COLONIAL FURNITURE 1921 Edition, Volume I, figure 116; New London County Furniture Exhibit 1974, catalogue #48.

Ht. 7' 9½" Wd. 42" Dp. 21"

P3741 Chippendale mahogany blockfront bonnet top chest-on-chest, the upper section with rococco carved shell and original carved open flame finials, original pine tree brasses, fluted pilasters; attributed to Benjamin Frothingham, Charlestown, Massachusetts, circa 1760-1780.

A Frothingham labelled blockfront chest-on-chest with related carved shell and open flame finials is illustrated ANTIQUES November 1952 Frontispiece.

Ht. 7'9¾" Wd. 41¾" Dp. 21½"

P4100 Rare Sheraton mahogany gaming table, the folding top reveals an inlaid checkerboard and backgammon board; when folded the table forms a square; one side of the frame pulls out with a brass bale handle to support the leaf; New York circa 1800-1810.

Ht. 29″ open Lg. open 39″ Wd. 20¾″

P3874 Hepplewhite mahogany mantle or shelf clock with fan inlaid case and intricate fretwork crest, kidney dial inscribed "Joseph Loring," Sterling, Massachusetts, circa 1791-1812.

Ht. 38¾″ Wd. 12¾″ Dp. 6¼″

P3308 Chippendale mahogany blockfront desk, bracket feet and scrolled center pendant, blocked and fan carved interior with flame pilastered document drawers; attributed to Benjamin Frothingham, Charlestown, Massachusetts, circa 1760-1780.

The attribution to Benjamin Frothingham is based on the distinctive interior which is identical to that on a labelled Frothingham secretary, ANTIQUES November 1952 page 393. Page 395, same issue, shows a Frothingham labelled chest of drawers with the same blocking, blocked bracket feet and pendant.

Ht. 42¾″ Wd. 40¼″ Dp. 23¼″ Wr. Lvl. 32½″

P3852 Chippendale mahogany five legged claw and ball foot card table, deep serpentine front and sides with square candle corners, narrow frame with concave and convex gadrooned border on front apron only, the frame supported on four gracefully shaped cabriole legs with a fifth swing leg in rear concealing an original secret drawer, the front legs and knee brackets are carved with assymetrical C-scrolls and acanthus leafage; the top is felt lined with recessed candle corners and scoop, choice mellow brown patina, New York circa 1760-1780.

The New York serpentine card table is considered the masterpiece of the New York pre-Revolutionary era. A scholarly presentation of this group by Morrison H. Heckscher appears in ANTIQUES May 1973, pages 974-983. This form with the narrow skirt and graceful cabriole legs relates to Type II in the Heckscher article and appears to be by the same hand as the Beekman tables in the New York Historical Society.

This table descended in the Varick family and was purchased from the estate of a direct descendant.

Ht. 27¾″ Wd. 34″ Dp. 16½″

P4086 Chippendale cherry dish top candlestand, ball and ring turned pedestal with beautiful and rare fluted column; Philadelphia circa 1760-1780.

Ht. 28″ Dia. 17½″

P4096 Hepplewhite mahogany secretary with satinwood panels bordering the drawers, upper case with Gothic doors and frieze, the drop panel in base and the center crest panel contain ovals of satinwood and mahogany, octagonal ivory escutcheons, original brasses; attributed to Judkins and Senter, Portsmouth, New Hampshire, circa 1800-1810. The secretary descended in the Brown family of North Hampton and in 1801 belonged to John Brown of North Hampton, New Hampshire.

Ht. 77″ Wd. 40¼″ Dp. 20½″

P563 Hepplewhite mahogany sideboard with wavy inlaid gallery top, sunburst inlaid medallions center the door and cupboards and are repeated on the sides; the end cupboard doors open from the base on brass quadrants; attributed to Stephen Badlam, Dorchester, Massachusetts, circa 1780-1800.

Ht. 39″ Lg. 60″ Dp. 23½″

P3800 Early Queen Anne birch lowboy with mariner's compass inlay centering top; sunburst inlaid center drawer; drawers, apron and top bordered by double line inlay; original engraved brasses. Massachusetts circa 1730-1745.

Described and illustrated in L. V. Lockwood COLONIAL FURNITURE IN AMERICA 1926 Vol I, page 350, fig. XVI (supplement).

Ht. 29″ Wd. 34¼″ Dp. 22″

P3943 Chippendale walnut lowboy, finely sculptured claw and ball feet, cyma scrolled apron, thumbnail bordered fan, original brasses. Salem, Massachusetts, circa 1750-1780. A feature of this lowboy is its shallow depth making it particularly feasible as a hall piece.

Illustrated FINE POINTS OF FURNITURE, EARLY AMERICAN page 197.

Ht. 31″ Wd. 36″ Dp. 18½″

P3686 Pair of Queen Anne cherry ball and claw foot side chairs, acanthus carved knees with crosshatched centers in the manner of Gilbert Ash, vase splats, wavy stiles and carved yoke crest rails; New York circa 1750-1760.

See Downs AMERICAN FURNITURE, QUEEN ANNE AND CHIPPENDALE plate 105 for a chair of this form.

Ht. 39″

P3884 Queen Anne curly walnut bonnet top highboy, original brasses, attributed to Benjamin Frothingham, Charlestown, Massachusetts, circa 1750-1760. The thumbnail bordered fans and the shape of the bonnet are characteristic of Frothingham's work.

Ht. 7′5″ Wd. 40″ Dp. 21″

P4103 Queen Anne cherry chest-on-frame, the fishtail scrolled apron and graceful cabriole legs ending in slipper feet form a beautiful silhouette, original brasses. Rhode Island or Connecticut circa 1750-1770.

Ht. 5′5″ Wd. 38″ Dp. 19″

P4213 Transitional mahogany serpentine front claw and ball foot bureau; the drawers are fronted by superbly figured solid crotch grain with original finely chased bale brasses; the drawers are flanked by columns inlaid with parallel lines and book inlaid panels; a center pendant contains a black and white inlaid fan; the box inlaid top borders are seen on a pair of card tables labelled John Townsend; a rarely beautiful golden patina accentuates the flowing grain of the drawer fronts. Newport, Rhode Island, circa 1780-1800.

Ex-collection Mr. and Mrs. Mitchel Taradash.

Illustrated ANTIQUES December 1946, pg. 394.

Illustrated "Arts and Crafts of Newport" by Carpenter, page 61.

Ht. 35¼" Wd. 41¾" Dp. 24"

P4115 Chippendale walnut and gilt mirror, original finely sculptured phoenix ornament and side leaves, retains the original bevelled glass; American or English circa 1750-1780.

Ht. 52½″ Wd. 24½″

P3329 Chippendale mahogany scroll top highboy with acanthus carved scrollboard, shell and vine carved center drawer and acanthus carved knees, original brasses, the apron bordered by scrolled volutes and centered by carved shell. Philadelphia circa 1750-1770. The superior proportions of this highboy as well as the superb color place this high in the ranks of the important Philadelphia highboy form. Ex-collection Mrs. Francis P. Garvan. Illustrated ANTIQUES "American Chippendale Furniture in Mrs. Garvan's Collection" January 1956 page 65.

Ht. 8′ Wd. 45½″ Dp. 22½″

Early glass door cupboard with original decoration, Pennsylvania circa 1800-1820. Illustrated "American Antiques from Israel Sack Collection" Vol. VI, page 1628. Bayou Bend Museum.

Pilgrim cherry or red gum folding trestle table, New York circa 1670-1700. Known as the General Philip Schuyler field table and carried by him in the Revolutionary Battle of Saratoga. Illustrated "Antiques" January 1934, pages 4 and 5. Exhibited New York Furniture, Metropolitan Museum of Art, catalogue #9. Illustrated "American Antiques from Israel Sack Collection" Vol. V, page 1368. Private collection.

William and Mary maple and pine desk on frame, Massachusetts circa 1710-1730. Illustrated "American Antiques from Israel Sack Collection" Vol. V, page 1262. Israel Sack, Inc.

William and Mary painted chest with trees, New England circa 1720. Exhibited Whitney Museum, Smithsonian Institution. Illustrated "American Painted Furniture," Dean Fales, page 41. Private collection.

historic mansions and saved them from destruction. He owned two homes built by Robert "King" Hooper, one in Marblehead (now the Marblehead Arts Society), the other General Gages headquarters in the Revolution "The Lindens" (bought by Mrs. George Maurice Morris and moved to Washington). The magnificent panelled room from the Lindens he sold to the William Rockhill Nelson Gallery where it serves as the background for their American collection.

The depression did not really hit the antique field until two years after the crash or late in 1931. Dealers like Israel Sack and Phillip Flayderman had huge inventories and major auction sales in New York by both these dealers and selections from the Francis P. Garvan collection in those two years were quite suc-

continued on page 1174

P3974 The glory of the New Republic is superbly depicted on the top of this Sheraton birdseye maple sewing table—the allegoric figure of liberty holding a liberty cap and a shield with 20 stars in one hand, the other embracing an eagle clutching arrows and laurel branches; above a banner reads E PLURIBUS UNUM and below a plaque reads AMERICA. The drawer, sides and back have allegoric scenes. The bulbous turned legs support turret corners and ring turned capitals. Choice amber patina. Boston or Salem, Massachusetts, circa 1810-1820.

Ex-collection Robert Lee Gill.

Illustrated "Living With Antiques" by Alice Winchester page 205.

Ht. 28¾″ Wd. 22½″ Dp. 17¼″

P4018 William and Mary walnut chest of drawers, with maple ball front feet and maple rear stiles, the four drawers have varied geometric panels, the second and fourth drawers with repeat octagonal panels, the third drawer with intricate panels with deeply bevelled background, original tear drop chased brasses and chased escutcheons, choice patina, the front stiles continue to the floor and are rounded to form a core for the bold maple flattened ball feet; Boston, Massachusetts, circa 1690-1710.

Ht. 36¾″ Wd. 39½″ Dp. 22⅛″

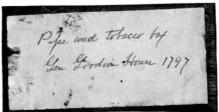

P4055 Pine pipe box with pinwheel carved motif on face, scalloped sides and back, the edges moulded and scribed, one drawer; Connecticut circa 1780.

The back retains an old inscription, "Pipe and Tobacco Box, Gen. Goodwin House 1797."

Ex-collection Philip Young, pioneer Boston collector.

Ht. 19½″ Wd. 5½″ Dp. 4″

P4079 William and Mary maple and hickory rush seat slat back side chair with six deeply bowed graduated slats, intact ball feet at front and rear, ball and ring turned frontal stretcher, a fine stately example; Philadelphia or vicinity circa 1710-1740.

Ex-collection Philip Young, pioneer Boston collector.

Ht. 47″

P4072 Queen Anne maple Spanish foot side chair of tall stately proportions; exceptional bulbous turned stretchers at side and rear with ball and ring turned frontal stretcher; slender violin splat; horned yoke crest rail and spooned profile; fine honey maple color; North Shore, Massachusetts, or lower New Hampshire circa 1730-1750.

Ht. 43½″

P4032 Rare walnut windsor table, circular top with deep dish rim, three flaring bulbous and ring turned legs joined through the top with wedged extensions, bulbous stretchers, choice mellow patina, Pennsylvania circa 1760-1790.

Ex-collection J. Stogdell Stokes.

Illustrated Wallace Nutting's "Furniture Treasury" plate 1303.

Illustrated "The Windsor Chair" Ormsbee, page 158.

Exhibited Philadelphia Museum of Art.

Ht. 26″ Diam. 17″

P4071 William and Mary cherry desk-on-frame, ball and ring turned legs with feet intact, box stretchers, drawer in frame and desk sections; Connecticut circa 1720-1750.

Ht. 41½″ Wd. 35¾″ Dp. 19¾″
Wrtg. Lvl. 30½″

P4024 Queen Anne maple porringer top tea table, turned tapering legs ending in pad feet, the maple has taken on a warm honey patina; Newport, Rhode Island, circa 1750-1770.

Ht. 26″ Wd. 33¾″ Dp. 23¾″

P4051 Queen Anne walnut wing chair with maple rear legs and frame, conventional form with chamfered rear legs which have lost 1½″ in height to receive casters, arrow turned stretchers, fine original finish and all knee returns; Massachusetts circa 1740-1760. The original linen undercover has been retained.

Ex-collection Philip Young, pioneer Boston collector.

Ht. 46½″ Wd. 34½″

1135

P4021 Chippendale curly maple desk with carefully selected figured grain, bracket feet with spurred brackets, center scrolled pendant with spurred brackets, the unusual interior is formed of four stepped back rows of small drawers; New Hampshire circa 1770-1790.

Ht. 41″ Wd. 36″ Dp. 18¾″ Wrtg. Lvl. 28¼″

P3730 and P4013 A virtual pair of courting mirrors in their original pine carrying boxes, rare small size, the decoration varies slightly in color and design but the mirrors are apparently by the same hand, imported from the Continent for the American market, circa 1790-1800.

Each 12½″ x 7¾″

P4022 Pair of brass andirons, bulbous columns with ring turned plinths and collars, flattened ball and ring top with flame tips, spurred legs ending in platformed pad feet; Philadelphia circa 1750-1770.

Ht. 17¼″ Wd. 10″ Dp. 17½″

P4034 Chippendale cherry tripod candlestand, stationary top of serpentine outline, urn shaped column, cabriole legs with platformed pad feet, serpentine outline at base of column, old or original finish; Massachusetts circa 1770-1790.

Ht. 25¼″ Top 16¾″ x 17″

P4073 Windsor small combback side chair, serpentine crest supported by raking bulbous turned columns, deeply bowed spindles, bold raking nicely turned legs, old or original black paint of great character; New England circa 1780-1800.

Ht. 36½″

P4028 Queen Anne cherry bonnet top highboy of graceful design and proportion; slender bandy cabriole legs ending in platformed pad feet, cyma scrolled apron, the center drawer of the lower case features a carved fan with scribed border; the related upper case drawer has a carved sunburst with scribed border, the highboy retains its original brasses and slender urn finials with carved flame tips; Connecticut circa 1750-1800.

The highboy bears a close relationship in form to examples owned by Mr. and Mrs. Joseph Hennage and in the Henry Ford Museum Connecticut Furniture Exhibit catalogue 1967, plates 84 and 85.

Ex-collection Philip Young, pioneer collector.

Ht. 7′ 2″ Wd. 38½″ Dp. 20″

P4057 Sheraton curly maple one drawer end table with birdseye maple veneered frame, turret corners; bulbous turned legs with attenuated bulbous feet, original finish, the drawer features an original, rare Bilston enamel pull depicting a rider on horseback in brilliant colors; Portsmouth, New Hampshire, or vicinity circa 1800-1810. The table is deeper than it is wide making it ideal for use as an end table.

Ht. 28¼″ Wd. 15″ Dp. 18¾″

P4053 Hepplewhite birch tall clock; the case is typical of the Willard school and is in fine original state; the delicate fretwork, finials and feet are intact; the enamelled dial is inscribed "DAVID WOOD, NEWBURY PORT"; the finish is a brick red stain which may be the original; made by David Wood, Newburyport, Massachusetts, circa 1800-1810.

Ht. 7′ 8¼″ Wd. 19½″ Dp. 10″

FURNITURE AND FURNISHINGS OF
JOHN BROWN, PROVIDENCE MERCHANT

John Brown (1736-1803) was the richest merchant in Providence. Until 1771 he was in business with his three brothers and with them was largely responsible for bringing Brown University to Providence. The Brown brothers, then John Brown himself after 1771, had extensive trade relations with Philadelphia, Boston, Newport and New York, and ordered furniture from Philadelphia and from John Goddard in Newport to furnish his houses. In 1786 he built the magnificent mansion in Providence, now the headquarters of the Rhode Island Historical Society.

This information has been assembled from two scholarly articles by Wendy A. Cooper in ANTIQUES magazine, February 1973, pages 328-339 and April 1973 pages 734-743.

The following group of furniture was purchased from a direct descendant of John Brown in unbroken line of descent, and it can be firmly stated that these items were originally the property of John Brown.

LINE OF DESCENT

1. John Brown (1736-1803) Merchant of Newport, Rhode Island.
2. Sarah Brown, daughter of John Brown (Died 1825), married Karl Friederich Herreschoff, Courtier at the Court of Frederick The Great, in 1801. They had six children.
3. Charles Frederick Herreshoff (name spelling changed) (Born 1809-Died 1888), son of Karl and Sarah Herreschoff, married Julia Ann Lewis (Born 1811-Died 1901) from Boston in 1833. Her father was a Merchant in Boston. They had nine children.
4. Caroline Louisa Herreshoff, daughter of Charles and Julia Herreshoff and grandmother of the descendant from whom we purchased the furniture, married Ebenezer S. Cheseborough, Civil War veteran, in 1866. Caroline Herreshoff Cheseborough died in 1924. Ebenezer called himself E. Stanton Cheseborough and came from Stonington, Connecticut.
5. Albert Stanton Cheseborough, son of E. Stanton and Caroline Cheseborough (Born 1868-Died 1916).
6. Wescott Cheseborough, son of Albert Cheseborough and descendant from whom we purchased the furniture, inherited the items directly from his grandmother, Caroline Louisa Herreshoff Cheseborough, since her son Albert predeceased her.

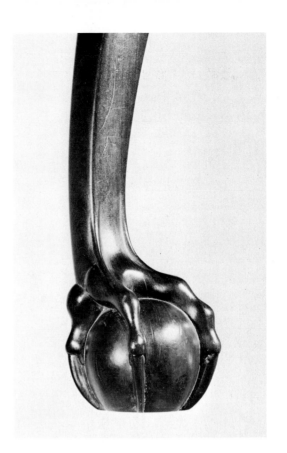

Original Furniture of John Brown

P4059 Chippendale San Domingan mahogany drop leaf table of rare small size, top of rectangular shape, cabriole legs with high taloned claw and ball feet, arched apron, original dark brown finish; attributed to John Goddard, Newport, Rhode Island, circa 1760-1765. The superbly sculptured claw and ball feet are identical to those on the pair of corner chairs made for John Brown and also attributed to John Goddard. One of the pair, property of Norman Herreshoff, is in the John Brown House, the other, now in a private collection, was illustrated P937 in Sack Brochure 23.

Ht. 27¼″ Wd. 12¼″ closed Dp. 17½″
           40¾″ open

Original Furniture of John Brown

P4063 Chippendale mahogany and gilt mirror of important size; scrolled crest and base of simpler outline indicating its origin early in the period; pierced and carved gilded shell centering crest, original finish and bevelled glass; English or American and bearing the label of John Elliott, Sr., Philadelphia circa 1758-1762. This mirror is the mate to one in the Norman Herreshoff collection illustrated in Wendy A. Cooper's article ANTIQUES February 1973 page 330. The labels on both mirrors have "Wholesale and Retail" handwritten on the printed form.

This mirror is undoubtedly one of two shipped from Philadelphia by Francis and Relfe on March 5, 1763. The invoice reads, "2 mahogany Sconce glasses with gilt edge and shell £ 9:06:00 [each]." Cf. ANTIQUES February 1973 page 332. The price noted on the label of Norman Herreshoff's mirror corresponds to this invoice.

Ht. 52¾″ Wd. 24¼″

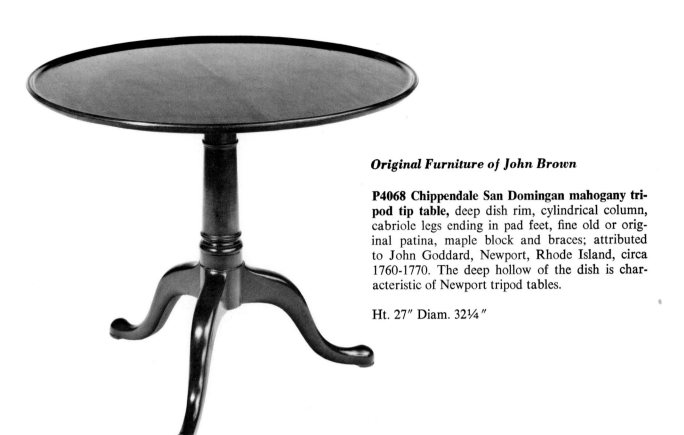

Original Furniture of John Brown

P4068 Chippendale San Domingan mahogany tripod tip table, deep dish rim, cylindrical column, cabriole legs ending in pad feet, fine old or original patina, maple block and braces; attributed to John Goddard, Newport, Rhode Island, circa 1760-1770. The deep hollow of the dish is characteristic of Newport tripod tables.

Ht. 27″ Diam. 32¼″

Original Property of John Brown

P4067 Rare or unique pair of brass and iron urn top andirons, the bulbous column is characteristic of the form associated with Rhode Island handiwork—concentric disc ring fronting the plinth; the iron bowed legs are fronted by round brass studs and end in pad feet, the back stops with urn tops matching the front finials are of iron; Rhode Island circa 1750-1770.

Ht. 20¼″ Wd. 11¾″ Dp. 19¾″

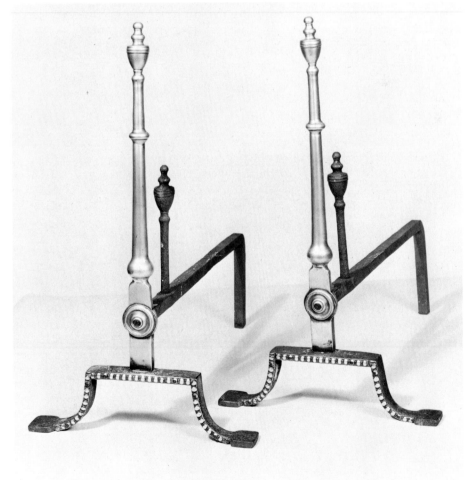

P4061 Hepplewhite mahogany serpentine front sideboard with recessed bowed cupboard section below the center top drawer; flanking this is a deep drawer with drawer above on one side, on the other one long door inlaid to simulate drawers, the drawers and cupboards bordered by choice pyramidal inlay; the center legs are canted to blend with the contour; graceful form and convenient low height; choice nut brown patina; Philadelphia circa 1780-1790.

John Brown's trade with Philadelphia was extensive and his records show evidence of ordering considerable furniture from that center to furnish his houses.

Ht. 38½″ Lg. 5′9″ Dp. 27″

P4064 Queen Anne mahogany bonnet top highboy, cabriole legs with C-scrolled inner borders, scooped center drawers of upper and lower case, beautiful warm light brown patina; Boston, Massachusetts, circa 1750-1760.

A family history on the back reads:

"This bonnet top highboy belonged to Mrs. Russel of Brookline, Massachusetts, great granddaughter of James Russel Lowell, Harvard."

Ht. 7′ 3″ Wd. 41″ Dp. 21½″

P4062 Chippendale walnut tall clock, broken arch top with carved rosettes and flame finials, the slender waist with arched door and the raised base panel with arched crest are flanked by fluted quarter columns, the brass spandrelled moon dial bears the plaque of the maker; Benjamin Morris, Hilltown, Pennsylvania, circa 1760-1780.

Ht. 8′ 4″ Wd. 18¾″ Dp. 11″

P4036 Chippendale San Domingan mahogany oval top tripod tip table, the surface of the cabriole legs have pointed ridges extending to the tips of the platformed feet, urn column, mint condition with fine dark brown patina, Boston or Salem, Massachusetts, circa 1760-1780.

Ht. 27½″ Top 22½″ x 16¾″

P4060 Chippendale mahogany and gilt "Constitution" mirror of rare small scale and slender proportions, broken arch top, the gilded rosettes with scrolled pendants, original phoenix ornament and side leaves, American or English circa 1760-1780.

Ht. 48″ Wd. 23¾″

P2632 Chippendale mahogany dish top tripod table with birdcage support; cabriole legs ending in superbly sculptured claw and ball feet; elliptical ball and ring turned column with tapering shaft; fine old patina; Philadelphia circa 1760-1780.

Ht. 27¼″ Diam. 34″

P4039 Chippendale mahogany ball and claw foot wing chair, horseshoe shaped seat frame, vertical flaring arms, bowed crest, finely modelled cabriole legs with acanthus carved knees centered by a floral medallion, beautiful amber patina, New York circa 1760-1780. The distinctive knee motif is identical to that on a New York corner chair, Bayou Bend Museum collection.

Ht. 47¼″ Wd. 38″ Dp. 31″

P888 Chippendale mahogany ball and claw foot side chair, vase shaped interlaced splat with diamond center and tassel in silhouette, crest rail with linen fold center, stop fluted stiles; Boston, Massachusetts, circa 1760-1780. This chair is the virtual mate to the chair made for President Joseph Willard of Harvard. Cf. Harvard Tercentenary Exhibition 1936, catalogue #252.

Ht. 37″

P4046 Chippendale mahogany mirror with scrolled crest and base, carved and gilded phoenix in crest, original glass and back; American or English circa 1760-1780.

Ht. 33″ Wd. 18¼″

P4023 Queen Anne San Domingan mahogany drop leaf table, oval top, cabriole legs with pointed knees and platformed pad feet, nicely scrolled apron; Massachusetts circa 1740-1770.

Ht. 29″ Wd. 44¾″ Lg. 47½″

P4047 Pair of Chippendale walnut and gilded mirrors with original cartouche ornaments, the broken arch tops have acanthus carving trailing the arch with egg and dart borders ending in carved rosettes with pendants; the mirrors are bordered by superb leaf and floral carving of cyma outline with an egg and dart outer border; the scrollboards and bases have applied gilded cartouches; the backplates for sconces are the original and the mirrors retain their original gilding. New York or English circa 1740-1760.

History:

1. Hendrick Rutgers married Catherine De Peyster in New York in 1730.
2. Mary Rutgers—fifth child of Hendrick and Catherine Rutgers (Note: Her brother was Henry Rutgers, founder of Rutgers University)—married Stephen McCrea (Born 1755) who was surgeon in Battle of Ticonderoga, Revolutionary War.
3. Mary McCrea—daughter of Stephen and Mary McCrea—married Timothy Hedges.
4. Mary Rutgers McCrea Hedges (born April 4, 1819) married Abraham Bogart Conger 1836.
5. Wilhemina De Peyster Knauth—granddaughter of Mary Conger.

This history is supported by a number of family letters and geneologies that will be provided to the purchaser.

The mirrors were on loan in the Boston Museum of Fine Arts until the end of 1968.

Ht. 60½″ Wd. 30½″

P4076 Queen Anne mahogany lowboy; the case with one long drawer, two shallow drawers below affording a case of slender depth, cyma shaped apron centered by typical Goddard-Townsend concave shell; beautifully modelled squared removeable cabriole legs ending in wafer pad feet; the top has a smooth top surface, the edge with half round moulding and connected to the case by a retaining moulding, beautiful mellow brown original patina, original brasses and structural blocks and braces; Goddard-Townsend, Newport, Rhode Island, circa 1750-1770.

Illustrated "Fine Points of Furniture, Early American" page 193.

Ht. 29⅝" Wd. 32¾" Dp. 21"

P4019 Chippendale mahogany pier mirror of outstanding quality, design and condition; the proportions are tall and slender, the frame outlined in egg and dart borders and side vines; the two sectioned glass is outlined by carved and gilded borders with gilded incised motifs at base and upper corners; the frieze is fronted by gilded bellflower drops in relief centered by a silhouetted fretwork panel with colored background; the broken arch top ends in carved rosettes and with the original phoenix center ornament perched on a carved and gilded plinth; probably New York circa 1750-1770.

A related mirror is illustrated plate 256 "American Furniture, Queen Anne and Chippendale in the Henry F. du Pont Winterthur Museum," Downs.

Ht. 78½″ Wd. 32½″

P4042 Sheraton mahogany dressing or serving table; serpentine front and sides, turret corners with waterleaf carved turrets in star punch "snowflake" background, ring turned capitals with star punch background; tapered reeded legs, pear shaped feet with ring turned cuffs; the frame is fronted by one drawer in center with oval veneered panel; the edges of the top are bordered by concentric rings, beautiful bronze patina; attributed to William Hook, Salem, Massachusetts, circa 1800-1810.

The Museum of Fine Arts, Boston, has four pieces made in 1808 as a wedding present to his sister Hannah. The work table of this group and a detail of the carving is illustrated in "Salem Furniture Makers, William Hook," ANTIQUES April 1934 pages 144-146.

Ht. 32½" Wd. 35¼" Dp. 20"

P4078 Federal mahogany and gilt mirror, pediment top, carved and gilded urn ornament, the crest and base with gilded metal lyre and musical motifs in relief, the original bevelled glass is bordered by metal studs and ring turned corners; Salem, Massachusetts, or English, circa 1790-1800.

Ht. 50" Wd. 19"

P4074 Sheraton mahogany sofa, the rectangular panel of the crest features a large oval panel of flame satinwood veneer framed in mitred and crossbanded border, the arms have moulded top surfaces and are supported by bulbous reeded arm supports, the bowed seat frame has a crossbanded veneered front, two of the four rear legs are reeded the same as the four front legs; Salem, Massachusetts, circa 1800-1810.

Ht. 38¼″ Lg. 6′ 4″ Dp. 26⅓″

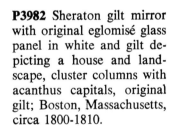

P3982 Sheraton gilt mirror with original eglomisé glass panel in white and gilt depicting a house and landscape, cluster columns with acanthus capitals, original gilt; Boston, Massachusetts, circa 1800-1810.

Ht. 33¼″ Wd. 19″

P4040 Hepplewhite mahogany pembroke table, oval top with line inlaid border, drawer at one end flanked by book inlay, square tapered legs each faced with figured birch or satinwood on two sides; Rhode Island circa 1780-1800.

Ht. 28″ Lg. 30″ Wd. 20¾″ (closed)
38″ (open)

P4029 Mahogany fire screen with gilt decoration, Chippendale in form with Federal influence; tripod base with finely sculptured claw and ball feet, C-scrolled borders, rosette and leaf carved knees; the spiral column is supported on a fluted urn, the fluted urn design and spiral repeated on the flame finial which has a gilt beaded base; the original large oval screen has a moulded frame with gilt beaded inner border enclosing a beautifully preserved silkwork embroidery—a cluster of flowers tied with a bowknot with an outer floral border in brilliant colors; original finish and gilding; Salem, Massachusetts, circa 1790-1810.

This fire screen descended in the family of Elias Haskett Derby of Salem and was obtained from direct descendants.

Ht. 61″ Screen 21½″ x 23″

Comparison of this screen with other Derby masterpieces in the Museum of Fine Arts, Boston, is rewarding.
1. The magnificent screen illustrated in Randall "American Furniture" plates 114 and A. The cabriole, the precision sculpture of the ball and claw feet and the C-scrolled borders suggest the same hand. Another interesting relationship is in the pattern of the embroidery, the bowknot in this example holding the cluster while in the Museum's example the basket suspends from a similar bowknot. The floral borders of both screens are also similar.
2. The superb dressing glass illustrated Hipkiss "M. & M. Karolik Collection" plate 136. The rosettes that border the glass and from which the drapery supports suspend are the same as the rosettes on the knees of this screen.
The form and carvings of this screen are more understated and less Classical in their expression, suggesting the theory that it slightly predates the richer McIntire example and served as the inspiration for Elias Haskett Derby or Elizabeth Derby to emulate on a more ambitious scale.

A SEYMOUR MASTERPIECE

P4058 Hepplewhite mahogany two drawer tambour desk; the tambours inlaid with bellflower drapery swags concealing small drawers and pigeonhole compartments retaining the original robin's egg blue paint; the two long drawers are fronted by mahogany veneer with carefully chosen figured grain, the Bilston enamel pulls with urn center motifs are of the period but not original to the piece; the drawers and tambours are flanked by pilastered inlaid columns; squared tapered legs with bellflower inlay and modified spade feet, pierced corner brackets, fine old or original finish; attributed to John Seymour and Son, Boston, Massachusetts, circa 1794-1804.

The attribution to John Seymour can be well supported. Comparison with the labelled example Montgomery "Federal Furniture" plate 184 shows the following related features:

1. The treatment of the inlaid drapery swags of the tambours.
2. The robin's egg blue paint of the pigeonholes.
3. The arrow inlaid detail of the top is identical on both pieces.
4. Each has an oval ivory escutcheon plate that locks the tambours as well as centering the two long drawers.
5. Large drawers veneered on white elm.

A remarkable relationship exists between this example and the tambour desk illustrated in Stoneman "John and Thomas Seymour" plates 14 and 15. In fact, with the exception of the inlaid border of the top edge, they appear to be identical. Both have a star motif centering the inlaid drapery swags, the dot dash inlay of the folding lid, the pilasters, brackets, bellflower inlay and spade feet are also the same. The Bilston enamel pulls are not original to this piece but are eighteenth century and identical in pattern with the related companion.

At some time in its career a framed writing slide had been adapted between the two sections fortunately enclosing and preserving the original flap lid except for small sections on each end which have been carefully restored.

Ht. 41″ Wd. 36¼″ Dp. 19½″ Wrtg. Lvl. 28″

P3764 and 4056

In brochure 23 we illustrated the mirror on the left (P3764). Recently we acquired its companion which, while not a mate, is patently by the same hand and which is for all practical purposes, the same size. Thus the mirrors will serve as a pair of a quality seldom rivalled. P4056 is illustrated in Wallace Nutting's "Furniture Treasury" plate 3032.

The mirrors are described as follows:
Sheraton gilt mirrors, baluster columns with acanthus capitals, crests centered by triangular eglomise glass panels supporting superbly sculptured eagles poised for flight and facing each other. Both have flaming torch end finials emanating from bases of varying design. Nutting shows the eagle holding glass beads which have evidently been replaced by the more proper drapery chains. American or English circa 1800-1810.

P3764   Ht. 49½" Wd. 22¾" Wd. (frame) 21"   P4056   Ht. 50" Wd. 23" Wd. (frame) 22½"

P4020 Sheraton mahogany octagonal top sewing table, octagonal case is fronted by one drawer and one sewing drawer, the turned tapering legs with cylindrical capitals and pear shaped castered feet, fine bronze patina; attributed to Nehemiah Adams, Salem, Massachusetts, circa 1800-1810.

Ht. 29¼″ Wd. 19¾″ Dp. 15½″

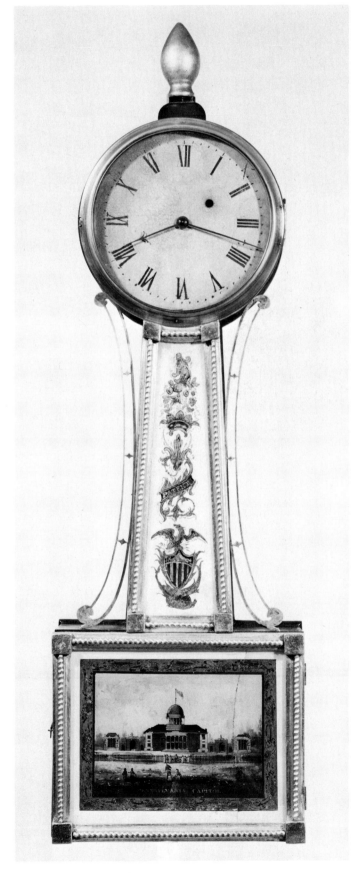

P4052 Gilt banjo clock with original eglomise glass panels, the door panel (with vertical crack) depicting a rare view inscribed "PENNSYLVANIA CAPITOL"; the waist panel depicting an eagle and shield and the word "PATENT." Since we know of only one other example by Aaron Willard showing this view, it is our opinion the damage to the glass is allowable and inoffensive. Boston, Massachusetts, circa 1810-1825.

Ht. 32½″ Wd. 10″

P4069 Chippendale applewood secretary desk, the base with four graduated drawers flanked by vine carved quarter columns, ogee bracket feet, the upper section with two doors forming a Gothic arch flanked by architectural fluted columns in bold relief, crested by overhanging ledge cornice with box shaped ends and center keystone; the highlight of the piece is the center of the interior which, together with the flame pilasters form an ingenious secret compartment. The center door is a masterpiece of naive creative or primitive art—the urn with scrolled handles of light wood stands out in bold relief. The patina is an amber tone of great depth and warmth. South Jersey or Pennsylvania circa 1760-1785.

Ht. 7' 2½" Wd. 38" Dp. 24" Wrtg. Lvl. 28½"

**P4070 Queen Anne cherry dropleaf dining
table** of rare large size, top of oval shape
with rounded edges and eight inch overhang
at ends allowing for convenience of seating,
apron with cyma shaped corners, turned
legs ending in slipper feet, fine old mellow
patina; New York circa 1740-1760.

The family history records its tradition of
ownership by Jonas Platt and its tradition
as the "Washington table" due to Washington's frequent visits to Colonel Platt's homestead in New York City.

Ht. 28¼″ Wd. 19″ closed Lg. 53″
Wd. 57½″ open

Family Inscription Under Top

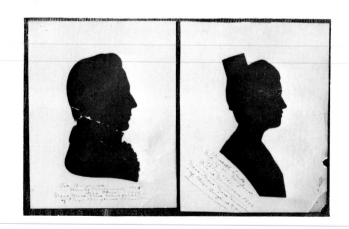

P4025 Chippendale walnut tall clock by Jacob Godshalk, Towamencin, Montgomery County adjoining Philadelphia, circa 1760-1770. Jacob Godshalk moved from Towamencin to Philadelphia before 1771 so the clock dates before 1770.

The case represents one of the most handsome specimens of Philadelphia area workmanship from the standpoint of proportion, carving and authenticity. The hood features the original cartouche and scrollboard carving, the waist has a carved concave shell cresting the scrolled arched door; the fluted quarter columns have raised scrolled carving at the front and sides of the plinths and carved capitals, a boldly scrolled panel fronts the base flanked by fluted quarter columns, ogee bracket feet; the brass spandrelled dial has a moon phase with deep blue background and "Jacob Godshalk—Towamencin" in the crescent.

Inside the door are silhouettes of the original owners John Bringhurst (1725-1795) and Elizabeth (Shute) Bringhurst (1735-1808), Germantown, Pennsylvania.

Ex-collection Mr. and Mrs. Mitchel Taradash.

Illustrated ANTIQUES magazine December 1946, page 304.

Ht. 8′ 4¾″ Wd. 19¾″ Dp. 10¼″

P4048 Small Chippendale mahogany card table, square moulded legs with corner brackets, one drawer, beautiful mellow brown patina; Massachusetts circa 1760-1780.

Ht. 28¼″ Wd. 31¾″ Dp. 15¼″

P4027 Rare or unique Queen Anne walnut slipper chair, the back is typical of an important group of New York chairs with bold shell crest, balloon splat with beaded cupid's bow base and wavy stiles that follow the outline of the splat, horseshoe seat, cabriole legs with modified drake feet, original seat frame and condition; New York circa 1740-1760.

A full scale chair of this design is in the Taradash collection, see ANTIQUES January 1953, page 47.

Ht. 35½″ Ht. seat 14½″

4017 Hepplewhite cherry tall clock crested by brass fretwork; moulded waist door with birdseye maple front; quarter columns with Corinthian capitals repeated on hood supports; fine amber patina; imported brass spandrelled dial inscribed "Thomas Hughes, London." New Hampshire circa 1810-1820. To our knowledge the attractive brass fretwork is a unique feature.

Ht. 7' 4" Wd. 19¼" Dp. 11"

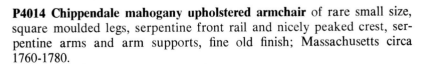

P4014 Chippendale mahogany upholstered armchair of rare small size, square moulded legs, serpentine front rail and nicely peaked crest, serpentine arms and arm supports, fine old finish; Massachusetts circa 1760-1780.

The chair has been upholstered in fine old needlework.

Ht. 37" Wd. 21¾"

P4045 Chippendale mahogany small mirror with scrolled crest and base, finely sculptured phoenix ornament in crest, original glass and back; American or English circa 1760-1780. Rare in this size and quality.

Ht. 20¼″ Wd. 12″

P3925 Chippendale San Domingan mahogany side chair of the highest order, gothic splat bordered by marginal carving, the crest rail superbly carved with floral center and acanthus ending in carved ears of three dimensional effect, the base with gadrooned carving, straight apron, acanthus carved knees and knee brackets, claw and ball feet; Philadelphia circa 1760-1780.

The back is virtually identical to the set of four paw foot side chairs in the Henry F. du Pont Winterthur Museum, Downs, "American Furniture" plate 129. There is also a close relationship to the Wharton chairs, Sack Brochure #25, page 30.

Ht. 37⅝″

P4030 Hepplewhite cherry tall clock, the case tastefully inlaid with fan quadrants in base and door with a repeat quadrant centering apron; fluted quarter columns flanking case and waist with satinwood stop reeds; the broken arch top has inlaid rosettes; flame finials with line inlay following the spiral; graceful apron and flaring French feet, beautiful amber patina, moon dial with sweep second hand. Philadelphia circa 1780-1800.

This clock descended in the family of Mary Sloan who married William Frick in Philadelphia in 1792. The superb set of four chair back Sheraton settee and chairs made for this couple is in the White House.

Ht. 8′ 1¾″ Wd. 20″ Dp. 10½″

P4044 Needlework sampler in original gilded frame with spiral border, the octagonal center panel depicts a landscape with house, basket and trees and is entitled "Wrought by Maria Butler in her 13th year, 1809." Massachusetts dated 1809.

Ht. 18¼″ Wd. 17¼″

P4043 Hepplewhite mahogany tripod tip table; an exciting original conception with shield shaped top, urn shaped column, bowed legs ending in spade feet; beautiful mellow brown patina; Massachusetts circa 1780-1800.

Ht. (tilted) 41″ Top 18″ x 22″
Ht. (closed) 29″

P4049 Sheraton mahogany barrel back Martha Washington armchair or lolling chair; a rare feature is the bulbous turned uprights which repeat the conventional bulbous turned arm supports; the incurvature arms have inlaid top surfaces, tapered turned legs, bulbous feet; Salem, Massachusetts, circa 1800-1810.

Ht. 41½″ Wd. 26″

P4077 Hepplewhite mahogany oval top pembroke table of exceptional quality and grace, accomplished by the delicate tapering legs and shallow frame; the legs are inlaid with overlapping husks and pellet drops with inlaid rosettes above, the crossbanded drawer front has the original elliptical handle, repeated on the blind drawer at the rear, concave moulded edge top, superb color and condition; New York circa 1780-1800.

The inlaid pellet drops relate to this feature on the labelled sideboard by William Whitehead, Sack brochure #18 page 650. The same feature occurs on the superb serpentine front sideboard Karolik Collection, Museum of Fine Arts, Boston, and the Whitehead labelled sideboard which belonged to Robert Fulton.

Ht. 28¾″ Lg. 31¼″ Wd. 19¾″ closed
                    38¼″ open

P4065 Sheraton mahogany two drawer end table with flame satinwood veneered drawer fronts, turret corners with ring turned columns, bulbous turned legs with parallel scribed rings; Portsmouth, New Hampshire, or vicinity circa 1800-1810.

Ht. 29″ Top 20¾″ x 19½″

P4041 Sheraton mahogany bureau and dressing glass; the case with three rows of drawers and a recessed cabinet section above with birdseye maple drawer fronts; the case is supported on reeded tapering legs with interrupted reeded turrets flanking the drawers; the rectangular mirror swivels on lyre shaped gracefully scrolled supports. Boston, Massachusetts, circa 1800-1815.

Ht. 6′ Wd. 42″ Dp. 21¼″

P2156 Hepplewhite bow front bureau with three panelled veneered branch satinwood fronts, birch top and sides, the top and panels bordered by crossbanded rosewood, the center panels centered by ivory inlaid octagonal escutcheons with a rectangular drop panel of branch satinwood centering the apron, French feet, original brass knobs with seashell centers, three knobs replaced. Portsmouth, New Hampshire, circa 1800-1810.

Ht. 38¾″ Wd. 41½″ Dp. 21½″

P4037 Rare Sheraton mahogany and gilt dressing mirror; the mirror with gilt spiral borders swivels on the stationary fluted gilded uprights which cant slightly to the rear; the eglomise glass panel is a gilt vase and flowers in an attractive blue field; the two drawers are cedar lined, the case is supported on French feet with a dot dash inlay above; the gilt is the original. Boston, Massachusetts, circa 1800-1810.

The form, while extremely rare, is not unique. A photograph of a virtually identical mirror owned by Israel Sack about forty years ago is in our files.

Ht. 23½″ Wd. 20″ Dp. 10″

P4035 Hepplewhite mahogany tripod tilt top candlestand, oval top, a solid board with finely figured grain and checkered inlaid border, urn and bulbous turned column, serpentine legs with rounded top facade centered by inlaid panels, spade feet; Massachusetts circa 1780-1800. A stand of superior quality and condition.

Ht. 29¾″ Top 21¾″ x 14¾″

P4075 Hepplewhite mahogany and gilt mirror with gilded broken arch pediment, original tall slender gilded urn with sprays of flowers and leaves, original gilded side leaves; New York circa 1780-1800.

Ht. 58″ Wd. 23″

Early pine decorated chest, Taunton, Massachusetts, circa 1725-1730. One of approximately a dozen surviving with the original decoration. Illustrated "American Painted Furniture" Dean Fales, page 39. Israel Sack, Inc.

Early pine open dresser with original painted decoration, Pennsylvania-German date 1787. Illustrated "Living With Antiques" Winchester, page 90. Illustrated "American Antiques from Israel Sack Collection" pages 1116 and 1301, Vol. V. Private collection.

Pair of side chairs by John Gaines, Portsmouth, New Hampshire, circa 1724-1735. Private collection.

William and Mary octagonal top tavern table, Pennsylvania circa 1710-1740. First piece purchased from Israel Sack by Mr. Taradash. Israel Sack, Inc.

cessful. Israel Sack was still buying collections in 1930 and 1931. His auction sale "One Hundred Important American Antiques" in 1932 in American Art Galleries proved disastrous. After that and other setbacks his inventory was wiped out, and he was left with no assets and considerable debt.

But this was not a man to be defeated. Recognizing that the field had become national, he moved his business and his family from Boston to New York. In 1933 my brother Harold, fresh out of Dartmouth College, but already with some experience in the field, joined my father. In 1934 I joined also as a fledgling with no knowledge or up to that point no interest in antiques. Little did I realize that my life would from that point on be interwoven with so great an intellect and force in the establishment of American antiques

continued on page 1175

William and Mary burl veneer highboy, Massachusetts circa 1710-1730. Illustrated ANTIQUES, January 1953, page 44. Illustrated "American Antiques from Israel Sack Collection" Vol. V, page 1265. Private collection.

William and Mary panelled chest of drawers, Boston, Massachusetts, circa 1690-1710. Illustrated "American Art from Israel Sack Collection" Vol. V, page 1132. Private collection.

Diminutive Queen Anne mahogany card table, Boston, Massachusetts, circa 1740-1760. Illustrated "American Antiques from Israel Sack Collection" Vol. IV, page 1068. Private collection.

Queen Anne walnut tray top tea table, Massachusetts circa 1740-1760. Private collection.

as a major art form as Israel Sack.

We rented a five story building on Madison Avenue (we couldn't fill one floor) on a commission basis. Harold and I fixed up an apartment on the top floor and for years drew no salary. The inspiration as well as the fundamentals came from observing the master. Instant knowledge became a necessity. There was no margin for error.

It was under those circumstances that Israel Sack first encountered Mr. and Mrs. Mitchel Taradash in 1933 or 1934. While not of unlimited resources, they were liquid and eager to form a collection. Needless to say Israel Sack was equally eager for a live client. A bond of friendship and trust was soon established that has lasted beyond their lifetimes to the next two generations and still continues. Israel Sack built a

continued on page 1252

P4192 and P4195 Pair of Hepplewhite mahogany secretaries; despite minor variations these secretaries have always been together and were unquestionably made as companions by one artisan; each top drawer of the base section fronts a butler's desk compartment; one with a single oval panel, the other with twin panels both bordered by the same inlay; the pyramid inlay of the cornice moulding is distinctive and rare; the flame effect of the figured veneer rising through the escutcheon line of both secretaries is similar as is the beautiful mellow brown patina; the dove of peace center ornaments are of the period. Salem, Massachusetts, circa 1780-1800.

Hts. 7′ 5″ and 7′ 6″ Wd. 43″ Dp. 22″

P4169 Chippendale walnut mirror of important size and beautiful slender proportion; the gilded carved mouldings of the broken arch top and the superbly carved original phoenix could barely be surpassed; incised floral gilding trails on the scrollboard from the base of the center plinth; the gilding of the crest carving, the side leaves and the pressed daisy motif on the baseboard is the original; mellow brown patina; New York or English circa 1760-1780.

This mirror descended in the Ten Eyck family of Albany and belonged to Ann Ten Eyck who married Matthew Vischer, Captain in Albany Militia in The Revolution.

Accompanying the mirror are two New York silver creamers bearing the Ten Ecyk and Vischer monograms.

Ht. 64″ Wd. 24¼″

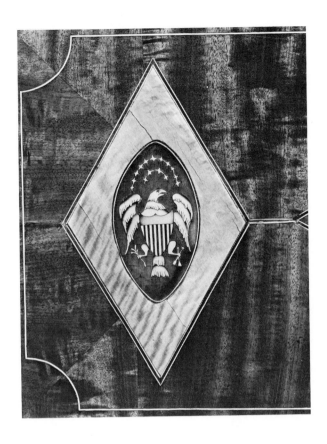

P4089 Hepplewhite mahogany and satinwood eagle inlaid linen press virtually identical in details to an eagle inlaid bureau in The Metropolitan Museum of Art, New York, bearing the label of Michael Allison. Choice mellow brown patina. Attributed to Michael Allison, New York circa 1795-1800.

Descended in the Demarest-Bradner families of New York and New Jersey.

Ht. 8'4" Wd. 45" Dp. 21"

**P4120 Chippendale birch four post tester
bed;** the foot posts are bulbous turned with
urn below ending in Marlborough feet;
original rails; headboard not original;
desirable mellow medium brown patina;
Massachusetts circa 1760-1780.

Ht. 83½" Lg. 75½" Wd. 56"

P4150 Pilgrim oak and pine bible box; the front
carved with intersecting lunettes, leaf and fleur-
de-lis with stipple background; the pine top has
serrated edges on the side and is secured on the
original quartered oak cleats with original rose
beaded nails that hinge from a dowel extension
of the back; the box has the warm, mellow color
of American light oak that has never been disturbed. This original aspect is highly prized by
collectors of Pilgrim furniture and is rarely found.
This box can be compared with examples by
Thomas Dennis of Ipswich. Ipswich, Massachusetts, or vicinity circa 1670-1690.

Ht. 8½" Wd. 27¼" Dp. 18"

P4146 Sheraton mahogany bow front serving table of rare small size; the case is fronted by two drawers flanked by cupboard doors each with flame satinwood panels contained in inlaid borders with cut corners and crossbanding; the delicate turned tapered legs with bulbous ring turned feet and cylindrical collars are in the tradition of Nehemiah Adams of Salem with satinwood panels fronting the stiles; the apron has an inlaid border with an arch under the center drawers; the top has a fine inlaid bordered edge; beautiful golden patina. Salem, Massachusetts, circa 1800-1810. Attributed to Nehemiah Adams or Nathaniel Appleton. Cf. ANTIQUES Magazine November 1933 "The Documented Furniture of Nehemiah Adams." We consider this table to be one of the finest expressions of the Salem Sheraton school.
Ht. 34¾″ Wd. 39¾″ Dp. 20¼″

P4085 Sheraton mahogany four post tester bed; slender bulbous reeded foot posts with acanthus carved leaves at base, above a bulbous carved urn with lamb's tongue panels framed by six arches formed by beaded columns with beaded collar; head posts plain tapered; the rails retain the original canvas; original nut brown finish. Salem, Massachusetts, circa 1800-1810. The width of over five feet is exceptional.

Ht. 7′3″ Lg. 6′9″ Wd. 5′1½″

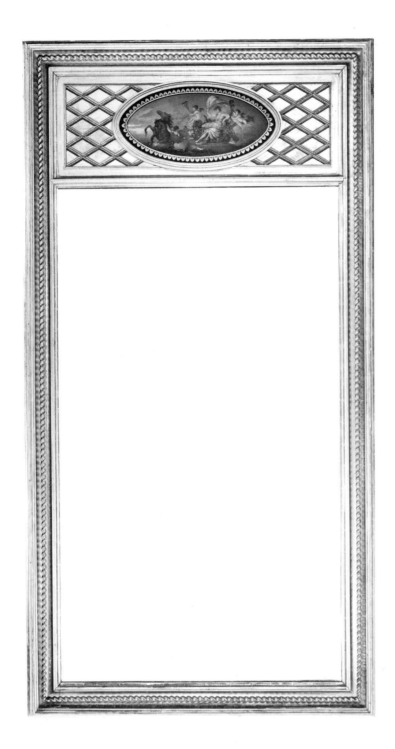

P4084 Sheraton gilt pier mirror of important size (nearly eight feet in height); the frame has a cove moulding on all four sides bordered by spiral gilt stringing; the crest panel is centered by an oval convex painting on wood depicting an allegorical scene of Minerva riding a chariot pulled by horses accompanied by cherubs; the painting is similar to that on Aaron Willard banjo clocks but is of exceptional artistry and beautiful pastel tones, the field for the panel is a repeat series of diamonds framed by spiral gilt stringing; the gilt, glass and back are the originals. Boston, Massachusetts, circa 1800-1815.

Ht. 94¾″ Wd. 49½″

P4129 Hepplewhite mahogany serpentine front side-board of Southern origin; the inlay is highly individual, the vine inlay on the stiles resembles that on Southern cellarettes and are capped by black and white daisy medallions; the serpentine center apron is fronted by half and quarter satinwood fans, the legs are tapered to a narrow point at the base, they are fronted by triangular blocked inlaid panels with bellflower motifs; beautiful mellow brown patina, the secondary wood is Southern yellow pine; an inscription on the back of one drawer reads "Repaired by C. Hellman, Hampton, Va. Feb. 16, 1904." Virginia circa 1780-1800.

Ht. 37″ Lg. 5′ 5¾″ Dp. 27¼″

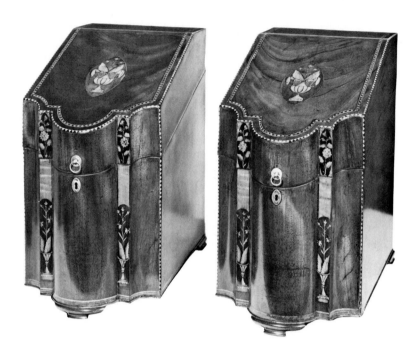

P4183 Pair of Hepplewhite mahogany serpentine front knife boxes; the pilasters are inlaid with vases of leaves and flowers and oval floral paterae; the lids are centered by large oval paterae with vase and floral inlay, while the lids and cases are bordered by tooth inlay; the cases are supported on ogee feet and retain their original slotted interiors and fine mellow patina. New York or English in origin circa 1780-1800. One of the finest pair of inlaid knife boxes we have had the privilege to own.

Ht. 16" Wd. 9" Dp. 15¼"

P4118 Brass mantle clock painted green with gilt acanthus foliage above plinth base; the plinth supports a bust of Washington; the clock dial inscribed "L. Mallet, Hor. de M. D. D. Orleans." French for the Amreican market circa 1800-1810.

Ht. 18½" Base 7¾" x 7¾"

P4102 Chippendale mahogany oxbow bureau with finely sculptured claw and ball feet; the knee brackets have finely scrolled cyma outline as does the center pendant; the moulded top has notched corners; beautiful golden patina. Massachusetts circa 1760-1780.

Ht. 34½″ Wd. 40½″ Dp. 25″

P4196 Chippendale mahogany blockfront bureau; bold convex and concave blocking; bracket feet with spurred inner outline; double lobed center pendant; original brasses; fine light brown patina. Massachusetts circa 1760-1780.

A family history pasted in a drawer reads:

This bureau belonged to my grandfather, John Waldron, of Boston, born 1799, also to his mother, Sarah Hooton Waldron, cousin of Elizabeth Hooton, who married General Joseph Warren.

   Elizabeth Warren Waldron

   Somerville (Massachusetts) June 24, 1930.

Ht. 31½″ Wd. 35¾″ Dp. 20¼″

P4186 Chippendale mahogany pembroke table; the top is serpentine in outline with turret corners with a moulded border; the beauty of the contour is enhanced by a superb swirling crotch figure and original warm brown patina; the frame contains one drawer; moulded legs; flat shaped cross stretchers with spade cutouts. Philadelphia circa 1760-1780. This table was purchased from the Countess Marguerite Pourtales, Newport, Rhode Island, having descended to her from her former husband who received it by reason of his relationship in the Willing-Spencer families in Philadelphia.

Ht. 28¾″ Lg. 31½″ Wd. 22½″ closed 43″ open

P4194 Chippendale walnut ball and claw foot lowboy; acanthus carved cabriole legs and scrolled knee brackets; nicely scrolled apron; chamfered fluted corners; moulded top with notched corners; the center drawer features shell, vine and floral carving in a deeply cut punchwork background; choice mellow brown old or original patina. Philadelphia circa 1760-1780.

Ht. 29″ Wd. 34″ Dp. 21½″

**P4125 Queen Anne walnut upholstered low
back armchair;** overupholstered balloon seat,
cabriole legs ending in pad feet; boldly bowed
incurvate arms with scooped arm rests and
scrolled terminals; serpentine arm supports;
bowed crest; fine old mellow brown patina.
New York circa 1740-1760. This chair is one
of a rare small group of New York armchairs
of this distinctive form. Other examples are in
the Henry F. du Pont Winterthur Museum, the
Metropolitan Museum of Art and the Charles
K. Davis collection.

Ht. 36″ Wd. 26″

P4180 Hepplewhite curly maple one drawer end table; clover leaf shaped top, tapered legs, with line inlaid and scribed borders; the case, drawer, legs and top have finely matched striped grain; original bale brass handle choice mellow patina of depth and warmth. New England circa 1780-1800. Illustrated Fine Points of Furniture, Early American page 269.

Ht. 26¾" Top 20" x 17½"

P4199 Hepplewhite mahogany "Martha Washington" armchair or lolling chair; nicely scooped arms; the inlaid panels adjoining the seat and the crossbanded cuffs of the tapered legs are an exceptional detail; light golden color. Massachusetts circa 1780-1800.

Ht. 47" Wd. 24½"

P4202 Hepplewhite mahogany serpentine front sideboard with recessed center bowed compartment flanked by concave turrets and canted center legs; the tapered legs have elongated diamond panel inlay with rectangular and diamond panels flanking the cupboards and drawers; the drawers, cupboards and top edge are bordered by black and white line inlay; fine bronze color; the secondary wood of long leaf pine determines its Southern origin. Virginia or North Carolina circa 1780-1800.

Ht. 42″ Lg. 5′ 11′ Dp. 26¼″

P4132 Brass and fire gilded mantle clock; full length standing figure of General Washington in uniform holding a sword in one hand; the enamel clock dial reads "Dubuc, Rue Michel-le-Comte, No. 33, a Paris"; the banner below reads "Washington, first in WAR, first in PEACE, first in the HEARTS of his COUNTRYMEN," above is a spread eagle and E. PLURIBUS UNUM. Made in France by Dubuc for the American market, circa 1800. The central importation point for these historic clocks was Baltimore. Dubuc was the best known maker and examples by him are in The White House and the Metropolitan Museum of Art, New York.

Ht. 19½″ Wd. 14½″ Dp. 5½″

P4122 Queen Anne mahogany blockfront kneehole desk of rare small size, the center recessed compartment is removable, the brass H-hinges for the arched panelled door are original as are the bat wing brasses; the center pullout drawer has diamond and scroll motifs. Salem, Massachusetts, circa 1735-1750. The desk descended in the Metcalf family. Miniatures of Eliah Wight Metcalf and Lydia Stedman Metcalf accompany the piece.

Ht. 31½″ Wd. 33¾″ Dp. 20¾″

P4182 Chippendale walnut high chest of drawers, platformed ogee bracket feet; fluted quarter columns; beautiful nut brown patina; a feature of this piece is the exceptional shell design of the original brasses, to our knowledge the pattern is unique. Philadelphia circa 1770-1790.

Ht. 67¼″ Wd. 43″ Dp. 21″

P4168 Chippendale mahogany mirror with scrolled crest and base; finely sculptured gilt phoenix silhouetted in scrollboard. American or English circa 1760-1780. This mirror is in the finest original state, the finish, gilt, glass and back never having been disturbed.

Ht. 42¼″ Wd. 22″

P4115 Chippendale walnut mirror with original carved and gilded phoenix ornament, side vines and arched cresting; the mellow brown patina has great depth and mellowness; the bevelled mirrored glass as well as the gilt are original. American or English circa 1760-1780.

Ht. 52½″ Wd. 24½″

P4106 Chippendale walnut tripod birdcage candlestand with circular dish top; urn column; nicely modelled cabriole legs with platformed pad feet. Philadelphia circa 1760-1780.

Ht. 28″ Diam. 21½″

P4198 Chippendale walnut slant top desk of desirable small size; fine interior with three rows of drawers each containing three concave blocked drawers; the top drawers fan carved; the center section is flanked by pilastered document drawers; blocked base drawers and scrolled pigeonholes; bracket feet with spurred inner outline; beautiful mellow light brown patina. North Shore, Massachusetts, circa 1750-1780.

Ht. 42″ Wd. 36″ Dp. 19″ Wrtg. Lvl. 31″

THE ROBB COLLECTION

HISTORY

OF

THE ROBB COLLECTION

It is true that there is nothing of greater value than a good name. A collection gains a reputation when the sum total of its excellence leaves a distinct impact on the collecting community. This name is achieved by careful selection and an uncompromising standard of quality and authenticity. A reputation is earned—it just doesn't happen.

The Robbs earned and gained this reputation over several decades. Nobody offered them anything but the best whether it be in form, design, proportion or a high standard of authentic condition.

The collection became a legend among the collecting world and when ANTIQUES Magazine published the collection in two parts, one in September 1967 and the other in April of 1968, Edith Gaines wrote the introduction by stating, "It would be hard to exaggerate the quality and importance of the furniture collection of Mrs. Walter B. Robb of Buffalo, New York. It has been many years in the forming, and though it has never before been published as an entity, many of its pieces—for example the Van Pelt lowboy and the Governor Wolcott sideboard—have appeared in books and magazines, either credited to former owners or labeled 'privately owned.' Astonishingly, others such as the extraordinary chest-on-chest in Figure 6 here and one of the two American Queen Anne beds to come to light (Fig. 4) have never been recorded. A large part of the collection consists of Newport and Philadelphia pieces of the Queen Anne and Chippendale periods, but the taste of Mrs. Robb and her late husband has always been catholic and it also includes some choice later examples. The unifying factor is a plus in almost everything: a more gracious relation of part to part, greater suavity in conception and execution of decoration, better over-all proportions than we find in the familiar prototypes."

The existence of this collection and its sale to our firm represents a few principles that are fundamental. First, there are great private collections in existence and they do come to market occasionally. This lends hope to the current collecting world that examples are available. Secondly, the choice of marketing has significance. The executors found it to be to the advantage of the estate to sell it to a leading specialist and dealer in the field. A most important point relevant to this is that the purchase of choice pieces at the prevailing price level from the best dealers and its eventual resale to the same outlet yielded exceptional monetary gains. Purchasing from dealers with a reputation invariably proves to be the right path. Quality pays off not only in aesthetic satisfaction but also in its financial by product or reward.

However, the heirs chose to keep some of the pieces as momentos. This constant syphoning of a segment of collections adds to the growing scarcity.

It is wise to acquire outstanding pieces when they become available. The opportunities arise in a diminishing degree. Therefore we in the capacity of our special area exerted our utmost to acquire the available portion of this collection to make it possible for the present collector to have his day.

We trust that these pieces will wind up once more in appreciative hands that will bestow the same affection and care as did the Robb family.

P4160 Chippendale mahogany piecrust tea table
with birdcage support. We consider this table a
masterpiece and, in our judgment, the finest example
extant. One of its outstanding features is the twin
flowers at each peak of the one piece top which is
just under three feet in diameter. The legs are superbly carved with long flowing acanthus emanating from
a fold over crest while the grasp of the sculptured
claw and ball feet and the thrust of the ankles ade-
quately support the large circular top. The column is
equally well carved with a tapering fluted column.
The greatness of the form is equalled by the original
undisturbed finish attributed to Thomas Tufft,
Philadelphia circa 1760-1780. The descent of this
tea table is as follows:
1. Dr. George Logan (1753-1821), physician, U.S.
Senator. Married Deborah Norris (1761-1839). Re-
sided at Stenton.
2. Albanus Logan (son) (1783-1839). Married
Maria Dickinson. Died at Stenton.
3. Gustavus George Logan (son). Married Anna
Armatt. Moved to Loudoun.
4. Robert R. Logan (son).
Illustrated in Hornor's "Blue Book of Philadelphia
Furniture" page 230 where it is described as the
Logan family tea table.
Exhibited in the Philadelphia Museum of Art May
1932 to October 1934.
Exhibited at Stenton, the residence of James Logan.

Illustrated "The Robb Collection" Part II, AN-
TIQUES, April 1968, page 487.

Ht. 28″ Diam. 35″

P4167 Queen Anne mahogany blockfront bonnet top chest-on-chest with curly mahogany fronts; the cabriole legs with wafer pad feet are finely modelled as is the cyma shaped center pendant; to our knowledge these elements are unique on a Massachusetts blockfront chest-on-chest. Another rare or unique feature is the formation of the fluted columns, each fluted segment is attached to its related drawer and moves with the drawer. The deeply carved shell and the bonnet top with cyma scrolled inner arch outline are typical of a number of Ipswich and Salem highboys. The flame finials are original and retain the original gilding; the batwing brasses and escutcheons are also original to the piece; the proportions and quality of craftsmanship are exemplary as is the careful selection of finely figured curly mahogany grain. Ipswich or Salem, Massachusetts, circa 1750-1760.

Illustrated "The Robb Collection" Part I, ANTIQUES, September 1967, page 325.

Ht. 7′9″ Wd. 38″ Dp. 22″

P4165 Hepplewhite mahogany and satinwood serpentine front sideboard; a masterpiece of the inlayer's art; the cupboard doors are inlaid with drapery and tassel motifs centered by inlaid urns; a drapery chain of tinted inlaid bellflowers interlace with the drapery and tassel inlay of the center cupboard and is repeated on the bowed center drawer; the drawer and cupboard doors are bordered by green tinted crossbanding with fan inlaid quadrants in the corners; the tapered legs are inlaid with tinted bellflowers and interlaced loops; the original label of Mills and Deming is behind the right hand cupboard door, Made by Mills and Deming, New York circa 1790-1795.

This sideboard was made for Oliver Wolcott, signer of the Declaration of Independence and first Governor of the State of Connecticut.

Ht. 48¾″ Wd. 74¾″ Dp. 32¼″

Exhibited "Loan Exhibition of New York State Furniture" The Metropolitan Museum of Art 1934, catalogue #118.

Exhibited "19th Century America" The Metropolitan Museum of Art, catalogue #4.

Illustrated ANTIQUES Magazine December 1928, Cover.

Illustrated ANTIQUES Magazine "The Robb Collection of American Furniture," September 1967, page 325, fig. 7.

Illustrated ANTIQUES Magazine October 1935, page 164.

THE ROBB COLLECTION

P4162 Chippendale mahogany blockfront kneehole desk or bureau table; two rows of three blocked drawers fitted with bat wing brasses, capped by long drawer with two convex carved shells with stop fluted centers and one concave shell; the center recessed cupboard is fronted by concave blocked and shell carved door; ogee bracket feet with C-scrolled marginal carved inner borders. Made by John Goddard or one of the Townsends, Newport, Rhode Island, circa 1760-1780. The careful craftsmanship, selection of choice close grained finely figured mahogany, and compact proportion represents the handiwork of one of Newport's finest craftsmen.

Illustrated "The Robb Collection" Part II ANTIQUES April 1968, page 484. This desk was purchased by us in 1948 from the Belknap family. Mrs. Belknap inherited it from her grandfather, Captain Morin, of Newport who married Miss Thorndike of Boston. The Thorndike family spent their summers in Newport.

Ht. 33″ Wd. 36¼″ Dp. 19¾″

1207

P4155 Chippendale mahogany ball and claw foot wing chair; horizontal roll flaring arms with dramatic thrust related to Philadelphia sofas of the period, serpentine wings and crest; the acanthus carving on the knees is centered by a bellflower chain with marginal C-scrolled borders; the finish is the original and undisturbed; the design of the carving as well as the claw and ball foot and C-scrolled borders are identical to those elements on the Gillingham armchair in the Henry F. du Pont Winterthur Museum, Downs #41. Attributed to James Gillingham, Philadelphia circa 1760-1780.

This chair descended in the family of Rowland Hazard of South Kingstown, Rhode Island. He married Mary Peace of Charleston, South Carolina, and took up residence at Peace Dale, Rhode Island. The chair descended in that family to Caroline Hazard who was president of Wellesley College 1899-1910.

Illustrated "The Robb Collection" Part I, ANTIQUES, September 1967, page 328.

Ht. 46½″ Wd. 39″

1209

P4156 Queen Anne walnut wing chair of tall stately proportion; the cabriole legs are of superior formation with smooth long graceful curve, slender ankle and finely modelled wafer pad platformed feet; the block and turned medial stretcher is generally considered indicative of Newport origin; the rear legs have chamfered edges; the patina is a beautiful light golden brown. Newport, Rhode Island, circa 1740-1760. The proportions of this chair are closely related to those of the Gardiner Newport wing chair.

Illustrated "The Robb Collection" Part I, ANTIQUES, September 1967, page 327.

Ht. 48¼″ Wd. 34½″

Queen Anne mahogany spinet; an inlaid maple panel above the keyboard reads "John Harris, Boston New England fecit"; flanking and above this panel are panels with diagonal black and white borders; the spinet is supported on four cabriole legs with bulbous turned vertical supports and square braces with moulded edges; the spinet cover and keyboard covers are equipped with original tulip shaped brass mounts; the keys and the instrumentation are original including the crow quills and strings; the piece retains the original mellow brown patina. Made in Boston 1769.

This spinet was given to Mary Malbone, daughter of Frances and Margaret Malbone of Newport, Rhode Island, when she married William Crooke in 1795. Mary Malbone Crooke was a sister of Elizabeth Malbone Breese and at the death of Mrs. Crooke (1815) the spinet was sent to the Breese house at Thames and Gidley Streets where it remained until 1902 when it was moved to 31 Old Beach Road, Newport. Accompanying the spinet is its original key with William Crooke's card attached on which is written "Key to Spinnet."

From "Colonial Dames and Good Wives" by Alice Morse Earle, pages 225-226: "The spinet is written up in the Boston Gazette, September 18, 1769. 'It is with pleasure that we inform the public that a few days since was ship'd for Newport a very Curious Spinet, being the first ever made in America, the performance of the ingenious Mr. John Harris of Boston (son of the late Mr. Jos. Harris of London, Harpsichord and Spinet maker, deceased) and in every respect does honor to that artist who now carries on the business at his house a few doors northward of Dr. Clarke's north end of Boston.'

This first American spinet is still in existence in a house in Newport on the corner of Thames and Gidley Streets. It has one set of jacks and strings. The hammers have crow quills which press on brass strings."

The article is not correct in stating this as the first spinet produced in America yet it is, to our knowledge, the only Queen Anne example bearing an American maker's name.

Illustrated "The Arts and Crafts of Newport, Rhode Island" by Ralph Carpenter, Jr., 1954, plate 50.

Exhibited "The Paul Revere Exhibit" Museum of Fine Arts, Boston, 1975, catalogue #135.

Ht. 32½" Wd. along rear edge 73"

P4166 Hepplewhite mahogany inlaid secretary; the upper section with swan's neck pediment ending in carved rosette terminals in the form of many seeded berries with leaf radiates; the glass doors have astragal shaped mullions with thirteen panes each; the lower case section has a butler's desk compartment fronted by twin oval inlaid panels; bracket feet. Attributed to William Appleton, Salem, Massachuetts, circa 1790-1810. Choice mellow patina.
The attribution is based on the relation of this secretary with the example bearing the label of William Appleton illustrated Montgomery "American Furniture" plate 178.

Illustrated "The Robb Collection" Part I, ANTIQUES, September 1967, page 324.

Ht. 7'11" Wd. 43" Dp. 24"

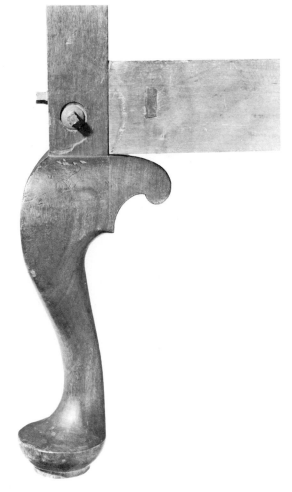

P4153 Queen Anne four post bed; walnut foot posts with finely modelled cabriole legs, platformed pad feet and voluted knee brackets; the posts turned and tapering; maple rails; square tapered maple head posts; original mellow light brown patina. Massachusetts or Rhode Island circa 1740-1760. The bed belonged to Major General John Thomas of Kingston, Massachusetts. Born 1724—died 1776. General Thomas was on George Washington's staff. On March 4, 1776, he was in command of the troops that fortified Dorchester Heights, over night, thus drove the British out of Boston.
Made Commander in Chief of the Army in Canada in the War of the Revolution March 1776.

A letter from the great-grand grandson of General Thomas, from whom the bed was purchased, accompanies the bed.
Illustrated "The Robb Collection" Part I ANTIQUES September 1967, page 324.
To our knowledge this is one of three Queen Anne four post beds known to exist. One example is in the Henry F. du Pont Winterthur Museum, the other in Colonial Williamsburg.

Ht. 7'1½" Lg. 6'5" Wd. 60"

P4163 Queen Anne walnut side chair with drake feet, acanthus carved knees and voluted knee returns; concave blocked seat frame centered by carved shell; the round stiles and crest is a rare feature in chairs of this group and form a powerful frame for the typical crest with boldly scrolled volutes centered by shell; the vase shaped splat with superbly figured crotch grain is fashioned from the solid; fine mellow brown patina. Philadelphia circa 1740-1760.

Illustrated "The Robb Collection" Frontispiece ANTIQUES April 1968.

Ht. 41½"

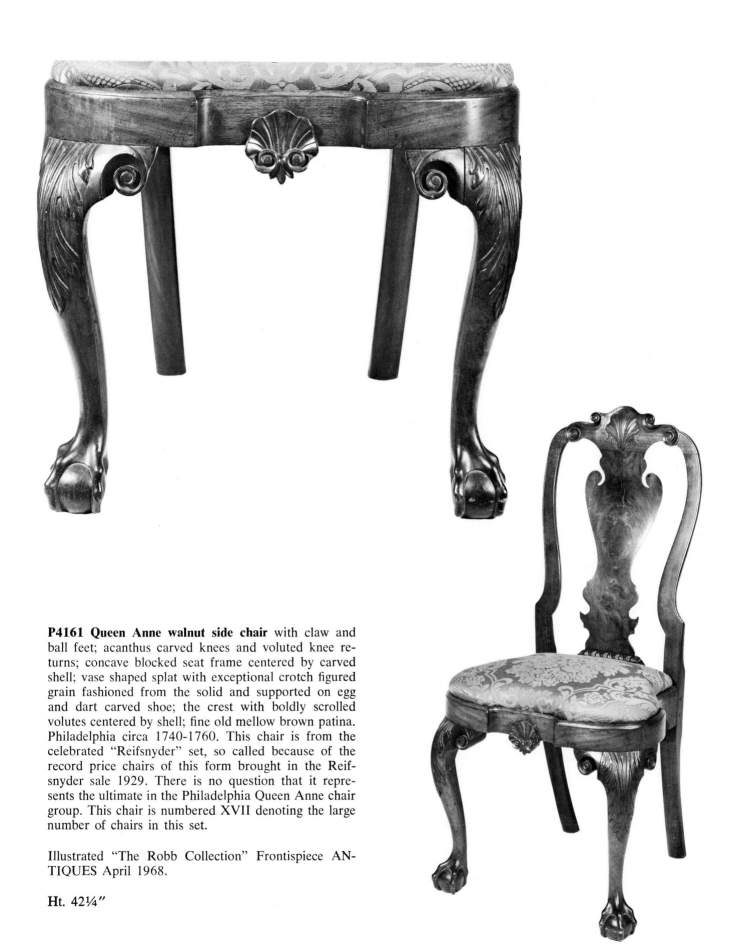

P4161 Queen Anne walnut side chair with claw and
ball feet; acanthus carved knees and voluted knee returns; concave blocked seat frame centered by carved
shell; vase shaped splat with exceptional crotch figured
grain fashioned from the solid and supported on egg
and dart carved shoe; the crest with boldly scrolled
volutes centered by shell; fine old mellow brown patina.
Philadelphia circa 1740-1760. This chair is from the
celebrated "Reifsnyder" set, so called because of the
record price chairs of this form brought in the Reifsnyder sale 1929. There is no question that it represents the ultimate in the Philadelphia Queen Anne chair
group. This chair is numbered XVII denoting the large
number of chairs in this set.

Illustrated "The Robb Collection" Frontispiece AN-
TIQUES April 1968.

Ht. 42¼"

P4159 Chippendale mahogany claw and ball foot wing chair; cabriole legs with acanthus carved knees and knee brackets and centered by daisy motif; the chair classifies as a masterpiece of the Philadelphia expression in the sweep of the horizontal roll arms, horseshoe seat and dramatically raking rear legs; the finish is the original. Philadelphia circa 1760-1770.

Illustrated Fine Points of Furniture, Early American page 67. Illustrated "American Antiques from the Robb Collection" ANTIQUES Magazine, September 1967, page 328, plate 13.

P4158 Pair of Chippendale ball and claw foot side chairs fashioned of dense San Domingan mahogany; the crests centered by foliated shells flanked by corded tassels ending in voluted roll ears; fluted stiles; the interlaced splats acanthus carved with scrolled volutes; the acanthus carved knees have carved cartouches above and both chairs retain their original carved knee returns; the center assymetrical shells carved in relief are an exceptional feature of these chairs. Philadelphia circa 1750-1770. The chairs retain a fine old dark patina.
Illustrated "The Robb Collection" Part I ANTIQUES September 1967, page 328.
Ht. 39"

P4157 Pair of Hepplewhite mahogany side chairs; the splats finely carved with elliptical fluted urns and drapery in oval frame; supported on flaring slats emanating from large carved sunbursts; moulded bowed stiles; moulded tapered legs; fine dark patina; the crispness of the carving and the selection of dense mahogany are of the highest quality. Newport, Rhode Island, circa 1780-1800. Illustrated "The Robb Collection" Part II ANTIQUES April 1968, page 485. Ht. 40″

P4154 Sheraton mahogany and bird's eye maple card table with lunette inlays and the rare occurrence of a fifth leg unusual in this regional form. Of excellent quality and design vying with the best of the Boston-Salem school. Massachusetts circa 1800-1810.

Illustrated ANTIQUES Magazine "The Robb Collection of American Furniture" April 1968, page 487, fig. 8.

Ht. 30″ Wd. 34″ Dp. 18¼″ closed·
                          36½″ open

P4164 Hepplewhite mahogany mirror of important size with original eglomise glass panel depicting a landscape scene; the swan's neck pediment has carved and gilded mouldings ending in carved rosettes and centered by a beautiful original gilded urn with sprays of flowers and wheat; the scrollboard is centered by an oval inlaid shell patera; the mirror glass and back are the originals as is the gilding. New York circa 1780-1810.

Illustrated ANTIQUES "The Robb Collection" Frontispiece April 1968.

Ht. 65″ Wd. 23″

P4138 Queen Anne mahogany bonnet top highboy; the center drawers of the upper and lower case sections have foliated carving with stipple background that is related to the carving on examples by Benjamin Frothingham; mellow light brown color; original bat wing brasses. School of Benjamin Frothingham, Charlestown, Massachusetts, circa 1750-1780.

Ht. 7' 1¾" Wd. 40½" Dp. 21¼"

P4151 Hepplewhite cherry blockfront sideboard; a rare and pleasing variation of the blockfront form; the single door of the center concave section has a rectangular beaded panel with cut corners; the convex blocked end sections each contain two drawers with circular ring turned brasses; the blocking is fashioned from the solid; square tapered legs; fine mellow color.. Connecticut circa 1780-1800. Inside the upper left drawer is the 1931 label and guarantee of Israel Sack which is shown below. Israel Sack made a practise of placing this label in the pieces he sold only in that year and we have since owned four or five similarly labelled examples. Each reflects the high standards of quality authenticity and stature that Israel Sack maintained 44 years ago and that we follow today.

Ht. 40½″ Lg. 53¼″ Dp. 24″

P4133 Chippendale San Domingan mahogany tripod candlestand; circular stationary top with deeply moulded dish rim; urn column with nicely tapering shaft; the cabriole legs have a leaf carving on the knees; fine bronze color. Newport, Rhode Island, circa 1760-1780.

Ht. 29″ Diam. 16″

P4137 Queen Anne cherry scroll top highboy of rare small scale; graceful cabriole legs with scrolled knee brackets and cyma scrolled apron; the center drawers of the upper and lower case sections have deeply concave carved fans with thumbnail borders; the broken arch top ends in carved rosettes; with flame finials; original brasses; amber color. Connecticut circa 1760-1780.

Ht. 6′ 11″ Wd. 37½″ Dp. 20″

P4187 Queen Anne walnut mirror of important size; the proportions and scrolling suggest a mid-century date; the veneered figure is exceptional in quality and tone; the scrollboard has a gilded shell and vines in relief; original bevelled glass. American or English circa 1750-1760.

Ht. 52″ Wd. 26½″

P4099 Chippendale curly maple slant top desk; four graduated drawers with original brasses; bracket feet with spurred inner outline; two tier stepped interior; fine mellow amber patina. Massachusetts circa 1760-1780.

Ht. 40¾″ Wd. 35″ Dp. 17″ Wrtg lvl. 30¼″

P4201 Early Queen Anne walnut mirror with original two section bevelled glass; the upper glass engraved with crown motif; mellow patina. English circa 1710-1730.

Ht. 33¼″ Wd. 15½″

P4086 Chippendale cherry tripod tilt top dish top candle-stand; a rare feature is the fluted shaft of the ball and ring turned column; the amber patina of this table is of exceptional warmth and mellowness; the appearance of a cherry candlestand of this excellence of modelling and quality is rare. Philadelphia circa 1760-1780.

Ht. 28″ Diam. 17½″

P4193 Hepplewhite mahogany tall clock; enamel moon dial inscribed "Nath'l Munroe, Concord"; beautifully designed case with original fretwork and exceptional gilded carved finials; the waist and base panel with inlaid panels and superb crotch figured grain; brass stop fluted quarter columns; French feet; choice old or original color. Made by Nathaniel Munroe, Concord, Massachusetts, circa 1800-1810.

Ht. 8′¾″ Wd. 20″ Dp. 9½″

P4136 Decorated Pennsylvania dower or bridal chest on hard pine background; the original decoration is characteristic of Lebanon County design particularly in the bulbous columns and heart corners; the background color is an attractive blue green with the floral twin panels on the top somewhat rubbed but preserved; bracket feet restored. Dated 1803, Lebanon County, Pennsylvania.

Ht. 28″ Wd. 49¼″ Dp. 23″

P4109 Pair of brass andirons; rights and lefts; rare or unique design; the hexagonal columns are supported on plinth base with bracket feet; beehive tops with back-stops of the same design. Signed "J. Davis, Boston" circa 1800-1810. Together with matching tongs.

Andirons: Ht. 19″ Dp. 24″

P4171 Queen Anne walnut mirror; in the finest original state including the two section bevelled glass, gilt and mellow finish; the scrollboard is attached to the ogival glass border in the William and Mary tradition and is centered by a gilded carved pressed shell with bellflower motifs. American or English circa 1740-1750. This mirror descended in a prominent Connecticut family, name to be given to purchaser.

Ht. 49½″ Wd. 17¼″

P4145 Chippendale mahogany side chair; boldly curved cabriole legs; the platformed pad feet have scribed line insteps, a feature seen on a number of Boston and Salem chairs; interlaced splat with scrolled volutes; the crest rail is centered by a leaf carved panel and has moulded ears; the slip seat is covered in contemporary needlework which appears to be original to the chair; the finish is original and untouched. Massachusetts circa 1750-1780. A virtually identical chair is illustrated in "New England Furniture at Williamsburg" by Barry A. Greenlaw, plate no. 54.

Ht. 38″

P4117 Chippendale maple bureau with slightly curly drawer fronts and original bale brasses; the ogee bracket feet are of distinctly Newport form with straightish inner outline. Newport, Rhode Island, circa 1760-1780.

Ht. 32″ Wd. 40″ Dp. 19½″

P4175 Portrait of Mrs. Charles D'Wolf (nee Mary Goodwin) 1783-1868. She married Charles D'Wolf in Bristol, Rhode Island, December 11, 1803. Artist unknown, original gilt frame. Rhode Island circa 1820-1830.

Ht. 34½″ Wd. 29″

P4111 Chippendale mahogany bureau with fluted quarter columns; veneered drawer fronts with beautifully figured grain; platformed ogee bracket feet; moulded top with retaining moulding below. Philadelphia circa 1760-1780. The careful craftsmanship and selecting of choice mahogany suggest the handiwork of a competent Philadelphia craftsman.

Ht. 34½″ Wd. 39¼″ Dp. 21¾″

P4189 Portrait of a man seated at table with pen in hand, subject unknown. American circa 1820-1830.

Ht. 20″ Wd. 18″

P4116 Sheraton gilt "tabernacle" mirror; original eglomise glass panel with scene of dancing girls in oval; framed by garlands of gilt flowers in white background; the frame has twin cluster columns each centered by spiral beading; original gilt and bevelled glass. Boston, Massachusetts, circa 1800-1810.

Ht. 43″ Wd. 15″

P4149 Sheraton mahogany three drawer end table; the drawer fronts appear to be curly birch with inlaid borders; flanked by ring turned turret pilasters supported on bulbous reeded legs and ring turned pear shaped feet in the Salem tradition; the top conforms in shape with a satinwood band bordering the top and a finely inlaid edge; beautiful mellow patina. Salem, Massachusetts, circa 1800-1810.

Ht. 29″ Wd. 19¾″ Dp. 17½″

P4121 Sheraton cherry tripod table with bird's eye maple frame; the top and case are bowed on all four sides and contain one drawer; the spiral turned column is supported on a circular platform base and spurred spider legs; an individualistic and pleasing original form. New Hampshire circa 1810-1830.

Ht. 28½″ Top 18″ x 18″

P4104 Sheraton mahogany bow front commode.
The characteristics of the handiwork of William Hook are evident in the carved waterleaf capitals with star punch background and concentric ring top borders. These motifs appear on the famous commode William Hook made for his daughter in 1807, see Randall "American Furniture" plate 70. The drawers are graduated from bottom to top with finely figured veneered fronts enhanced by a beautiful rich bronze patina and retaining the original eagle's head brass knobs. The case is supported on slender reeded tapered legs and columns effecting a graceful and successful proportion seldom seen on a bureau or commode of this period and size. Attributed to William Hook, Salem, Massachusetts, circa 1800-1815.

Ht. 42½" Wd. 51" Dp. 25"

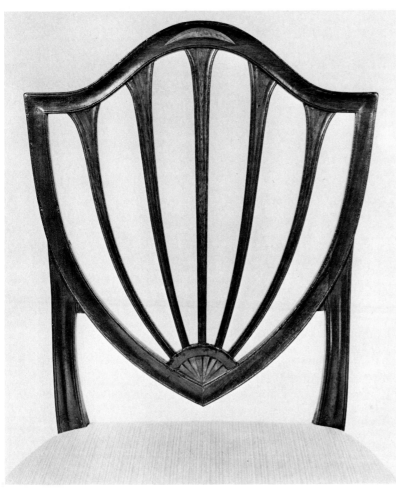

P4170 Set of seven Hepplewhite mahogany shield back chairs consisting of one arm and six side chairs; the back contains five moulded slats flaring at top with a fan inlaid crescent at base; moulded tapered legs; H-stretchers; the crests are centered by an unusual crescent inlay; the armchair with serpentine arms and moulded serpentine arm supports; mellow brown patina and fine condition. Salem, Massachusetts, circa 1780-1800.

Armchair   Side chairs
Ht. 38½″ Wd. 22½″ Ht. 37½″

P4185 Sheraton mahogany inlaid card table of rare or unique design; bowed front with serpentine sides; three panelled satinwood front with repeat panels on serpentine sides; the tapered legs each have satinwood panels instead of the usual reeding with cylindrical collars and superb flower pot inlaid panels fronting the plinths above; diagonal inlaid top borders and finely turned feet complete the composition. Salem, Massachusetts, circa 1800-1810.

Ht. 28¾″ Wd. 39″ Dp. 18″

P4123 Miniature portrait of Mrs. John Biddle; in black and gilt frame. Mrs Biddle was the great grandmother of Lieutenant William Shepherd Biddle. Probably Philadelphia early 19th century.

Ht. 7½″ Wd. 6¾″

P4114 Pair of Sheraton mahogany side chairs; Gothic moulded interlaced splats; the rectangular panels in the arched crests have drapery carving in star punch background in the tradition of Samuel McIntire; plain tapered legs; fine old or original finish. Salem, Massachusetts, circa 1800-1810. Descended in the Allyn family and purchased by us from descendants.

Ht. 36¾"

P4083 Hepplewhite cherry fire screen with oval screen; attached to the screen is a scrolled candle shelf; spider legs; bulbous turned column. Connecticut circa 1800.

Ht. 46" Screen 18" x 13½"

P4130 Hepplewhite mahogany inlaid pembroke table; oval top with finely figured grain and inlaid border; one end contains a drawer; the other a false drawer each with oval panels and flanked by fan inlaid paterae; the tapered legs are beautifully inlaid with flaring bellflower with etched black lines and crested by a scribed leaf. New York circa 1780-1800.

Ht. 28″ Wd. 19″ closed Lg. 32½″
39½″ open

P4179 Pair of Sheraton mahogany armchairs; bowed crests; the vertical slats with flaring terminals have scribed borders; the serpentine arms with bold scrolled voluted terminals are exceptional; moulded tapered legs; the chairs are in mint condition with the original dark brown patina. Salem, Massachusetts, circa 1800.

Ht. 36″ Wd. 22¼″

1244

P4144 Portrait of Lieutenant John Joliffe Yarnall who served under Admiral Perry and was lost with the "Epervier" August 1815. The portrait is in the original carved and gilded frame. Accompanying the portrait is Lieutenant Yarnall's sword made and inscribed "W. H. Hershmann and Sons, Makers, Philadelphia." The blade is beautifully engraved with patriotic motifs on both sides. The portrait and the sword were purchased by us from direct descendants of Lieutenant Yarnall.

Portrait: Ht 24¾″ x Wd. 20½″
Sword: Lg. 32″

P4143 Hepplewhite mahogany rare triple top game table; one top surface contains an inlaid checkerboard with arrow inlaid border when opened; the other top surface is plain; one drawer in the case with inlaid border; square moulded legs; mellow color. Massachusetts circa 1780-1790.

Ht. 29¾″ Wd. 31½″ Dp. 15¾ closed
Dp. 31½″ open

P4184 Pair of Hepplewhite mahogany shield back armchairs; the moulded shields each enclose four bowed slats with thumbnail carving radiating from a floral carved crescent; the tapered legs have bellflower inlaid fronts, reeded sides and end in spade feet; fine bronze patina. New York 1780–1800.

Ht. 37¾″ Wd. 26″

P4100 Rare Sheraton mahogany game table; the case with finely figured grain is almost square when closed, supported on four turned tapering legs with bulbous feet and concave ring turned collars in the New York tradition; one side with bale handle and drawer telescopes to support the folding leaf; when open the leaf contains an inlaid checkerboard; the case contains a recessed compartment with inlaid backgammon board. New York circa 1800-1810.

Ht. 29½″ closed Wd. 20¾″
29″ open

Dp. 19½″ closed
39″ open

P4101 Chippendale San Domingan mahogany oxbow bureau; while uncommonly large size, it is in perfect proportion; the careful craftsmanship and finely modelled bracket feet show the handiwork of a first rank Massachusetts artisan; mint condition with original bale brasses and dark old or original patina. Massachusetts circa 1760-1780.

Ht. 32½″ Wd. 42½″ Dp. 22¼″

P4141 Queen Anne walnut tray top tea table of rare diminutive scale; gracefully modelled cabriole legs with voluted knee brackets; platformed pad feet; flattened arch aprons on all four sides; mellow light brown patina. Salem. Massachusetts, circa 1740-1760.

Ht. 26″ Top 23⅛″ x 15½″

P4200 Queen Anne San Domingan mahogany small drop leaf table; finely modelled cabriole legs with platformed wafer pad feet; voluted knee brackets and flattened arch aprons. Boston, Massachusetts, circa 1750-1760.

Ht. 27″ Lg. 36½″ Wd. open 36⅜″
closed 14″

P4197 Chippendale mahogany side chair; the strapwork design of the splat, the crosshatched crest panel and the moulded ears are typical of Goddard-Townsend handiwork; mellow brown patina. Newport, Rhode Island, circa 1760-1770.

A companion chair with slight variations is in stock and illustrated Sack brochure #20, page 16. It would make an excellent companion.

Ht. 37½″

P4126 Chippendale mahogany tripod tip and turn candlestand; circular one piece top with crisply moulded dish rim; finely turned ball and ring turned column with tapering shaft and ogival ring turning below; well modelled cabriole legs with good lift to the ankles and bulbous platformed feet; beautiful mellow light brown patina. Philadelphia circa 1760-1780.

Ht. 28¾″ Diam. 22½″

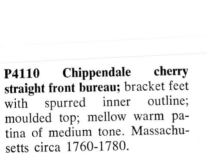

P4110 Chippendale cherry straight front bureau; bracket feet with spurred inner outline; moulded top; mellow warm patina of medium tone. Massachusetts circa 1760-1780.

Ht. 34″ Wd. 37½″ Dp. 20″

P4095 Chippendale mahogany tripod candlestand; stationary top with deeply moulded dish rim; the spiral column relates to the banisters on Salem staircases and is related to the column on the Derby fire screen Sack brochure #26, page 30; fine old nut brown finish. Salem, Massachusetts, circa 1760-1780.

Ht. 28″ Diam. 15¾″

P4097 Hepplewhite octagonal top one drawer end table; the top case and drawer of burl veneer while the tapered legs are each veneered with similar burl on all four sides; the wood has taken on a rich, deep patina of great warmth and mellowness. Massachusetts circa 1780-1800.

Ht. 27¼″ Top: 18½″ x 13½″

Chippendale walnut and gilt pier mirror, American or English circa 1750-1760. Illustrated "Living with Antiques" Alice Winchester, page 91. Illustrated "American Antiques from Israel Sack Collection" Vol. VI, page 1474. Israel Sack, Inc.

Queen Anne walnut veneer bonnet top highboy, Boston, Massachusetts, circa 1735-1745. Private collection.

Chippendale mahogany marlborough foot pembroke table, Philadelphia circa 1760-1780. Illustrated "Fine Points of Furniture, Early American" page 249. Metropolitan Museum of Art.

Queen Anne walnut side chair, Philadelphia circa 1750-1760. Illustrated "Living With Antiques" Alice Winchester, page 91. Illustrated "American Antiques from Israel Sack Collection" Vol. V, page 1289. Private collection.

great collection of Americana for the Taradashes. It was built like the pioneers built our nation, with sacrifice, ingenuity and perseverance, with devotion to uncompromising standards of authenticity, quality and inspirational artistry. It was big game hunting only the prey was masterpieces and the hunters roamed wherever the masterpieces appeared.

Some years later the Taradashes built the beautiful Colonial home in Ardsley on Hudson to house their collection which became nationally famous. Many of their great pieces were in major exhibits, publications and their home was shown in several issues of "Living With Antiques."

When Mr. Taradash passed away in 1972, Mrs. Taradash called on us to help her in appraising the collection and to purchase those things she would no

continued on page 1253

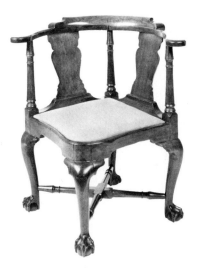

Queen Anne walnut corner chair, Newport, Rhode Island, circa 1740-1760. Illustrated ANTIQUES June 1946, page 358. Illustrated "American Antiques from Israel Sack Collection" Vol. IV, page 1088. Private collection.

Chippendale mahogany ball and claw foot bed, Massachusetts circa 1750-1780. Illustrated "American Antiques from Israel Sack Collection" Vol. V, pages 1266 and 1267. Private collection.

Chippendale mahogany octagonal top candle-stand, attributed to John Townsend, Newport, Rhode Island, circa 1760-1780. Illustrated "Arts and Crafts of Newport" Ralph Carpenter, page 53. Illustrated "American Antiques from Israel Sack Collection" Vol. IV, page 1084. Private collection.

Pair Chippendale walnut "Constitution" mirrors, American or English circa 1750-1770. Private collection.

longer use. Over the past several years we have had the privilege to reacquire a considerable number of items from the collection. The most interesting thing to me is that with all the knowledge that has been gleaned from scholarship and research since the collection was formed, not one piece from that collection can be judged as below museum level.

The relationship of Israel Sack with the Taradashes was the epitomy of what a dealer-collector relationship should be — based on their mutual love of true art and high standards.

Mrs. Taradash passed away in 1981. She was as much a connoisseur as Mr. Taradash and a purist to the highest degree. She loved Israel Sack and transferred that love to Israel Sack's sons Harold, Albert, Robert and to his grandson, Donald. She

continued on page 1310

THE JOHN FULTON SIDEBOARD
AND COMPANION KNIFE BOXES

1254

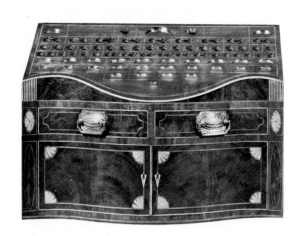
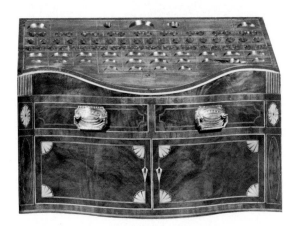

A FEDERAL MASTERPIECE

Partial label
Fulton Sideboard

Complete label
#1449, Sack Brochure 18

P4286 and 3025 Hepplewhite mahogany serpentine front inlaid sideboard and companion knife boxes, made and labelled by William Whitehead, New York circa 1790-1810.

The sideboard is the epitomy of grace and harmonious composition, the center legs and stiles are canted to create a knife blade effect, the bellflower inlay with connecting loops and the diamond escutcheons have pellet drops as pendants, the end cupboard doors, recessed cupboard doors and concave turrets have fan inlaid quadrants, with inlaid rosettes and book inlay flanking the drawers, original mellow brown patina of great depth and mellowness.

The knife boxes are made as companions, the fronts of conforming serpentine shape, with simulated drawers and cupboards, and inlaid patterns to match the similar arrangement on the sideboard. Both the sideboard and knife boxes retain the original chased octagonal brasses.

To our knowledge the knife boxes are unique.

History of descent of sideboard and knife boxes:

1. John Fulton (1739-1832)—Red Hook, New York.

Signed Revolutionary Articles of Association 1775. Judge of Common Pleas Court of Dutchess County. His Colonial home, built about 1796, is an official State historic site.

2. Ephraim Fulton (1783-1856)—Red Hook, New York.
3. Elisha Ephraim Fulton (1824-1903)—Red Hook, New York.
4. John Parker Fulton (1866-1930s)—Red Hook, New York.
5. Ethel Fulton Gallagher (1895-Still living January 1976)—Red Hook, New York.

The sideboard is closely related to the sideboard in the Karolik Collection, Museum of Fine Arts, Boston. It is our opinion that William Whitehead fashioned the Karolik sideboard rather than Matthew Egerton to whom it was attributed.

The partial labels on this Fulton family sideboard are established as those of William Whitehead by comparison with the complete labels on a related sideboard illustrated Sack Brochure 18, #1449.

A SALEM MASTERPIECE

P4287 Chippendale walnut bonnet top highboy with claw and ball feet; cabriole legs with ridged knees and scrolled voluted knee brackets; graceful cyma scrolled apron with spiral carved volutes; the center drawers of the upper and lower case sections each feature a carved fan of rare beauty and conception, the fan formed of alternating flutes and reeds creating an undulating effect with complementary scribed line border; bonnet top with original flame finials; the drawers retain the original brasses and a warm ruddy patina. Salem, Massachusetts, circa 1760-1770.

Descent of this highboy follows:

1. Captain John Stephenson, Sea Captain, Portland and Gorham, Maine. Married Tabitha Longfellow in 1771. Tabitha was the daughter of Stephen Longfellow (Henry Wadsworth Longfellow, the poet, the grandson of Stephen Longfellow).

2. Stephen Stephenson, son of Captain John Stephenson, born Gorham, Maine, December 28, 1778, married Harriet Storer, October 7, 1806.

3. Harriet S. Storer, daughter of Stephen Stephenson, born March 15, 1817, married George Motley of Lowell, Massachusetts, December 18, 1850.

4. George Motley, Lowell, Massachusetts, son of George Motley.

P4285 Queen Anne maple wing chair; conventional form but rare in maple which has acquired a ruddy patina; the ankles thrust well forward into the pad and the plain square rear legs are Rhode Island characteristics. Newport, Rhode Island, circa 1740-1760.
This chair was purchased some years ago by Jess Pavey from the Brown family of Providence.

Ht. 44½″ Wd. 33½″

P4232 Chippendale mahogany small serpentine bureau with richly figured veneered fronts; original bale brasses; ogee bracket feet; mellow brown patina. Salem, Massachusetts, circa 1770-1790.

Ht. 34¼″ Wd. 37½″ Dp. 20″

Ht. 44½″ Wd. 33½″

P4266 Primitive portrait of young boy whittling on tulipwood panel in original black and gilt frame. New England circa 1800-1820.

Ht. 30″ Wd. 24″

P4238 Chippendale mahogany bombe bureau; ogee bracket feet with finely scrolled inner outline; center pendant; overhanging moulded top with notched corners; original brasses; dark brown patina. Massachusetts circa 1750-1780.
Ex-collection Robert Lee Gill.

Ht. 33¼" Wd. 41" Dp. 21½"

P4259 Set of 8 Chippendale mahogany ball and claw foot chairs consisting of two armchairs and six side chairs; the carved splats are of typical Boston design with daisy motif in center and C-scrolled edges with fringe carving, the incurvate arms have moulded terminals and arm supports, the chairs retain the old or original dark brown finish, the ball and claw feet are finely sculptured with swept back talons. Massachusetts circa 1760-1780.

The fact that few Massachusetts ball and claw foot armchairs are known makes their appearance in a set of this size a distinct rarity. The set was illustrated in B. Kerfoots ad in ANTIQUES, June 1927, and later owned by Israel Sack.

P4208 William and Mary maple desk box on frame; the frame contains one drawer and is supported on fine ball and ring turned legs with ball and ring turned box stretchers; bulbous feet; slant lid hinged from the top with original butterfly hinges and concealing a simple interior; beautiful warm ruddy patina. Massachusetts circa 1710-1730.
Ex-collection Mr. and Mrs. Mitchel Taradash.

Ht. 32½″ Wd. 27¼″ Dp. 19¼″

P4231 Queen Anne maple Spanish foot side chair of tall slender proportion; rush seat finely turned bulbous and ring turned frontal stretcher with parallel row of bulbous turned stretchers on each side; moulded stiles and horned yoke crest; fine maple color. North Shore Massachusetts or New Hampshire circa 1730-1750.

Ht. 43″

P4207 Pilgrim maple two drawer Hadley chest; one of the earliest forms; described by Luther as the "Hatfield" type and attributed by him to John Allis who died in 1691. It varies from the larger conventional group by the case and stiles being fashioned entirely of maple with the original pine lid. The stiles terminate in integral turned feet, and the initials KK are contained in diamond frames in the end panels rather than the center panels of the larger group. Apparently by the same hand as the AA chest, No. 21 (Luther) made for Abigail Allis, born Hadley 1672, also the EA chest, No. 4 (Luther) made for Elizabeth Allis, born 1679. Made in Hatfield or Hadley, Massachusetts, circa 1680-1700.

Illustrated "The Hadley Chest" No. 44 by Luther.

Ex-collection Mrs. S. R. Bertron, Oyster Bay, Long Island.

Ex-collection Mr. and Mrs. Mitchel Taradash.

Ht. 39¼″ Wd. 47″ Dp. 19¾″

P4229 Pilgrim maple and pine ball foot chest of drawers retaining the original buttermilk red paint; four drawers bordered by early single beaded mouldings; deeply chamfered panelled sides; elliptical ball feet in front; stiles in rear; pre-dovetail construction of the drawer sides suggests 17th century origin. Massachusetts circa 1690-1710.

Ht. 38¼″ Wd. 40¾″ Dp. 19½″

P4228 William and Mary maple ball foot bureau; four rows of drawers, the top row divided; the original ball feet are secured on a central dowel pin in the same manner as the feet of William and Mary highboys; the finish is a warm ruddy maple of depth and mellowness. Massachusetts or Rhode Island circa 1700-1720.

Ht. 37¼″ Wd. 36¾″ Dp. 20″

P3772 Pair of William and Mary iron and brass andirons, baluster and ring turned columns, probably Dutch, circa 1680-1700.
Ht. 17″ Dp. 20½″

P4223 William and Mary highboy of walnut and maple with burl veneer fronts of beautifully chosen textured figure, the drawers with herringbone borders; the trumpet legs are superbly turned with flaring trumpets and inverted cup capitals; the arched and cyma shaped outlines of the front and side stretchers conform to the complementary cock beaded outlines of the aprons; the proportions are exemplary and the piece retains the old or original patina. Massachusetts circa 1710-1730.

Ex-collection Mr. and Mrs. Mitchel Taradash.

Illustrated "Living With Antiques" Alice Winchester, page 90.

Illustrated ANTIQUES January 1953, page 44.

Ht. 61¼″ Wd. 39″ Dp. 22″

1266

A MASSACHUSETTS MASTERPIECE

P4215 Chippendale mahogany claw and ball foot bed; the front posts with finely sculptured bold claw and ball feet; removeable knee caps each with acanthus carving crested by scrolled cartouche and with floral carved ends; slender fluted tapering posts; original maple octagonal head posts and pine headboard; original rails except front rail; original untouched finish. Massachusetts circa 1760-1780.
Ex-collection Mr. and Mrs. Mitchel Taradash.
Belonged to Mrs. Bradlee Smith of Brookline, Massachusetts, a direct descendant of William Penn.

Ht. 8'1″ Lg. 6'5½″ Wd. 56½″

P4206 Classical bridal "lighthouse" clock retaining the original white and gilt decoration; the tapering cylindrical waist contains an oval powder blue panel inscribed "Simon Willard's Patent, Roxbury"; the square base panel is fronted by a door with a classical scene; gilded ball feet; glass dome with fluted terminal; the dome encloses the brass works fronted by an enamelled dial; alarm wheel and bell. Made by Simon Willard, Roxbury, Massachusetts, circa 1820-1830.
Ex-collection Mr. and Mrs. Mitchel Taradash.
Illustrated ANTIQUES January 1953, pg. 47.

P4204 Sheraton mahogany bow front sideboard; the center cupboards and bottle drawers feature oval veneered panels; the drawers above are flanked by small square drawers with serving slide above; the case is supported by slender tapered reeded legs with bulbous feet; the stiles above have crossbanded panels and the top has a crossbanded edge; the piece retains a beautiful mellow brown patina. Attributed to Nehemiah Adams, Salem, Massachusetts, circa 1800-1810.

Ht. 43″ Wd. 5′10¼″ Dp 26¾″

P4264 Needlework embroidery on silk entitled CHARITY, scene with mother, children, landscape and village in octagonal border surrounded by garland of flowers supported by white dove; inscribed LOUISA BELLOWS, in original gilt frame with spiral border. Connecticut circa 1808.

Louisa Bellows was the daughter of Josiah and Rebecca Bellows. She was born in Walpole, New Hampshire, July 16, 1792, and died in South Boston, August 28, 1878. This fine needlework is of important size. The brilliant colors of the embroidery are beautifully preserved. The glass mat inscribed LOUISA BELLOWS, CHARITY is a replacement. The original glass is preserved and will be furnished to the purchaser.

Ht. 24½" Wd. 30¾"

P4276 Sheraton mahogany card table; bowed front and sides with turret corners; the frieze and turret corners are veneered in panels of flame satinwood; panels flanking the legs and the bowed center have crossbanded borders, the top edge with intricate checkered inlaid border; the bulbous reeded legs are capped by inverted ringed urns also capping the bulbous feet; mellow golden color. Portsmouth, New Hampshire, circa 1800-1810.

Ex-collection Max Israel.

Ht. 30" Wd. 35½" Dp. 17½"

P4241 Hepplewhite mahogany inlaid tambour desk; the case with two drawers fitted with Bilsted enamelled handles; the oval ivory escutcheons on the two drawers and repeated behind the flap lid to lock the tambours are features of Seymour's handiwork; the tambours are inlaid in a drapery bellflower pattern; bellflower inlaid tapered legs, pierced corner brackets; the pigeonhole interiors retain the original robin's egg blue paint. Made by John Seymour and Son, Boston, Massachusetts, circa 1794-1804. Beautiful satiny brown patina. Comparison with the example labelled by John Seymour and Son in the Henry F. du Pont Winterthur Museum (Montgomery " Federal Furniture" figure 184) leaves no doubt of the authorship.

Ht. 51½″ Wd. 37½″ Dp. 19½″

IT IS INTERESTING TO COMPARE THE INLAID BELLFLOWER GARLANDS ON THE TAMBOURS WITH THOSE OF THE LABELLED SEYMOUR CARD TABLE ON THE FOLLOWING PAGE.

A JOHN SEYMOUR MASTERPIECE

P4225 Hepplewhite mahogany demilune card table bearing the original label of "John Seymour and Son, Creek Square, Boston"; the frieze has repeat series of bellflower garlands, the bellflowers graduating in size and tied to bowknots; the top edge and apron bordered by curly maple or satinwood while curly maple or satinwood panels form the background for bellflower inlay on the tapered legs; the legs end in modified spade feet; bordering the top is a pellet and dot inlay; superb golden brown patina. Made by John Seymour and Son, Boston, Massachusetts, circa 1790-1800.

This table serves as a significant discovery, being, to our knowledge, the first labelled Seymour piece to appear in 40 years and which represents one of three known labelled pieces, the other two being tambour desks in the Henry F. du Pont Winterthur Museum and Cluett collections. The bellflower drapery pattern is the same as on the tambour shutters of several examples, the modified spade feet are seen on attributable examples (cf. Stoneman, Nos. 14, 25, 30). The pellet and dot inlay of the top is the same as the edge of the writing lid on the Stout tambour (cf. Stoneman, No. 11).

Ht. 28¾" Wd. 36" Dp. 18"

1273

P4254 Chippendale mahogany wing chair;
square stop fluted legs and box stretchers;
serpentine wings with straight sides and serpentine crest; the crusty original finish on
the legs is a desired protection to the authenticity of this rare Newport form. Newport,
Rhode Island, circa 1760-1770.

The unupholstered views show the chair
with the original linen undercover and web-
bing when first in our possession.

Exhibited "American Art from American
Collections" The Metropolitan Museum of
Art 1963, catalogue #40.

Ht. 47½″ Wd. 34¾″

A NEWPORT WING CHAIR

P4265 Pair of pastel portraits depicting Captain John Collins (1752-1824) and Mary (Stuart) Collins (1756-1811) by Benjamin Blyth, Marblehead, Massachusetts, circa 1780-1790. Captain John Collins married Mary Stuart December 1776. The pastels on pillow tacking background are in original black and gilt frames.

A letter from the Frick Art Reference Library dated October 5, 1956, supports the attribution to Benjamin Blyth and relates this portrait of Mrs. John Collins to the Blyth portrait of Mrs. Joseph White owned by the Essex Institute.

Ht. 23″ Wd. 17″

P4282 Queen Anne maple tea table; rectangular top with cyma shaped corners; squared cabriole legs ending in pad feet; the table has acquired a mellow patina of great depth and warmth. Rhode Island or Connecticut circa 1750-1760.

Ht. 27¾″ Top 31¾″ x 26½″

P4213 Transitional mahogany serpentine front claw and ball foot bureau; the drawers are fronted by superbly figured solid crotch grain with original finely chased bale brasses; the drawers are flanked by columns inlaid with parallel lines and book inlaid panels; a center pendant contains a black and white inlaid fan; the box inlaid top borders are seen on a pair of card tables labelled John Townsend; a rarely beautiful golden patina accentuates the flowing grain of the drawer fronts. Newport, Rhode Island, circa 1780-1800.
Ex-collection Mr. and Mrs. Mitchel Taradash.
Illustrated ANTIQUES December 1946, pg. 394.
Illustrated "Arts and Crafts of Newport" by Carpenter, page 61.

Ht. 35¼" Wd. 41¾" Dp. 24"

P4237 Sheraton mahogany four post bed, the foot posts with spade feet, leaf carved urns and bulbous reeded columns with leaf carved bases; octagonal birch head posts, maple rails rabbeted for canvas; arched headboard with scrolled voluted terminals ornamented with brass rosettes; the tester frame has gilded borders and slate gray facades; the bed is in a rare state of preservation, with the original nut brown finish and all parts original. Salem, Massachusetts, circa 1790-1810. According to the former owner the bed was purchased from the Belknap family of Salem. Its width of virtually five feet makes it practical for use as a double bed.

Ht. (to top of canopy) 7′4¾″ Lg. 80″ Wd. 59½″

P4248 Set of six Sheraton mahogany side chairs; finely carved backs with acanthus carved and fluted stiles with rosette carved terminals; the center uprights with plume carving and fan spandrels. New York circa 1800. A pair of armchairs made to supplement the set is available. This is one of the finest designs of a New York Sheraton chair. A chair of this pattern is in the Metropolitan Museum of Art.

Ht. 36½"

P4219 Queen Anne mahogany bonnet top highboy; scooped drawer in lower case section; inverted cup and acorn spiral finials. This highboy expresses the love of simplicity and slender vertical proportion of a Massachusetts artisan. It is in a rare state of preservation with the original warm mellow brown patina, original brasses and finials. Massachusetts circa 1740-1760.

Ht. 7′4½″ Wd. 39¼″ Dp. 22½″

P4278 Chippendale mahogany block front bureau; the drawers with bold round blocking retain the original large willow brasses; bracket feet with blocked inner outline; scrolled center pendant; fine light brown patina. Massachusetts circa 1760-1780.

Ht. 32½″ Wd. 36″ Dp. 21¼″

P4220 Chippendale mahogany mirror with scrolled crest and base; the crest with carved and gilded shell in silhouette. American or English circa 1760-1780.

Ht. 45½″ Wd. 25″

P4235 Hepplewhite curly maple one drawer stand of rare refinement and beauty; the square top has a beaded edge, crossbanded and inlaid borders and a central diamond motif; the beaded edged drawer has herringbone crossbanding and the original oval chased handle; the selection of evenly striped figure, the exceptional slender proportions and the warm mellow patina of great depth make this an outstanding example. Massachusetts circa 1780-1800.

Ht. 27″ Top 17½″ x 17¾″

P4233 Mahogany thermometer with brass plate running the gamut from Freezing to Fever Heat, inscribed "Charles Poole, New York." Early 19th century.

Ht. 17″ Wd. 2½″

P4247 Sheraton mahogany settee of rare small size; the crest is the shape appearing on the great sofas carved by Samuel McIntire with a rectangular center panel and serpentine wings. In this example the center panel contains a leaf carved center with fan spandrels; the wings have crotch veneered figured grain; moulded serpentine arms; reeded arm supports with leaf carved urn bases; bulbous reeded legs; old or original patina. Salem Massachusetts, circa 1800-1810.

Ht. 38" Wd. 4'8½" Dp. 20¼"

P4263 Watercolor painting depicting Anne E. Crehore of Milton, Massachusetts, in yellow dress with dog at her side, figures, a river and view of the Boston State House in background, a tree with the initials of her father William M. Crehore, at age 33 "WMC AE 33, 1836" inscribed on tree, the panel below reading "A. E. Crehore, Æ ᵀ 1 Year & 6 Mo. 1836 J R Pinxt," in original frame.

Ht. 16″ Wd. 12¼″

P4227 Pair of mezzotints depicting George Washington and General Marion "The Swamp Fox" in carved and gilded frames; the frames bear the label of R. Cribb, glass and picture frame maker Holburn (England) circa 1800-1810.

Ht. 14¾″ Wd. 13¼″

P4230 Pair of bronze busts depicting General George Washington in uniform and Count D'Estaing, on cylindrical marble plinths with brass bases, beaded mounts and draped chains, the placques by a Frenchman with limited English vocabulary read "WASINGTON and "COMTE D TSTAING." French for the American market circa 1780-1800.

Ht. 7″ Diam. 3″

P4269 and P4267 Pair of oil portraits depicting Charles Gyles, merchant of Newport, Rhode Island 1780-1849, and Mrs. Charles Gyles, in original frames. Rhode Island circa 1820-1840.

Ht. 37¾" Wd. 31¾"

P4281 Queen Anne cherry tray top tea table; the bulged apron with cyma scrolled outline and fishtail spurred central motif is typical of a group of Connecticut examples. Connecticut circa 1740-1770.

Ht. 26" Wd. 28½" Dp. 19¾"

P4210 Sheraton mahogany Martha Washington armchair; beautifully shaped incurvate hoop arms with bulbous reeded arm supports; serpentine seat frame flanked by cylindrical satinwood veneered plinths; bulbous reeded legs; serpentine crest; fine color. Porstmouth, New Hampshire, circa 1800-1815.

Ht. 41″ Wd. 25½″

P2900 Classical gilt small convex mirror, finely sculptured eagle perched on fluted plinth; original gilding; American or English circa 1800-1815.

Ht. 30″ Wd. 17″

P4283 Queen Anne walnut lowboy; cabriole legs with stockinged drake feet; cyma scrolled apron; moulded top with notched corners; the underside of the top contains the inscription "Repaired by J. Janvier, April 20, 1799." Philadelphia or Odessa, Delaware, circa 1750-1770.

John Janvier, Senior (working circa 1770-1801), was one of Delaware's best known cabinetmakers. He was Philadelphia trained and moved to Odessa, Delaware about 1770.

Ht. 28¼″ Wd. 34″ Dp. 21¼″

P4212 Queen Anne walnut side chair; the back is superbly modelled with rounded undulating stiles and crest centered by shell and scrolled volutes; the vase shaped splat has an openwork pattern with acanthus carving; the cabriole legs have shell carved knees while the knee brackets are acanthus carved with scrolled voluted terminals; light golden color. Philadelphia circa 1750-1760.
Ex-collection Mr. and Mrs. Mitchel Taradash.
Illustrated ANTIQUES June 1946, pg. 358.

Ht. 42¼"

P4293 Chippendale mahogany ox-bow desk with superbly sculptured claw and ball feet with swept back talons; center fan and scrolled pendant; the slant lid features a fine crotch grained figure; the interior has the unusual feature of drawers above as well as below the pigeon-holes and is centered by a row of blocked drawers, the top drawer fan carved; the brasses are contemporary but not the first set; beautiful mellow brown patina. Salem, Massachusetts, circa 1760-1780.

Ht. 43½″ Wd. 41½″ Dp. 23″

P4295 Pair of Chippendale mahogany side chairs; beautifully shaped cabriole legs with acanthus carved knees and claw and ball feet with swept back talons; interlaced splat with linenfold and tassel; mellow brown patina. Boston, Massachusetts, circa 1760-1780.

Ht. 37¼"

P929 Chippendale mahogany drop-leaf table; circular top with rounded edge; cabriole legs with pointed knees ending in claw and ball feet with thin nicely sculptured knuckles; bulged apron with cyma shaped outlines, mellow brown patina. North Shore, Massachusetts, circa 1760-1780.

Ht. 27" Lg. 44"
Top 43½" open
      15½" closed

P4299 Pair of diminutive carved and gilded sconce mirrors; the floral bases are centered by iron sockets to hold sconce arms; old gilt and aspect. Continental circa 1800.

Ht. 16½″ Wd. 7½″

P4257 Hepplewhite mahogany card table with flame satinwood veneer; bow front with serpentine sides; bowed front is centered by an oval satinwood panel in crossbanded frame and flanked by finely figured satinwood; the top and apron are bordered by a rare pattern of intricate inlay with the rippled dotted element tinted blue green; delicate tapered line inlaid legs. Massachusetts circa 1780-1800.

Ht. 29¼″ Wd. 35¾″ Dp. 17¼″

P4280 and P4262 Cherry shelf clock with enamelled kidney shaped dial inscribed "Aaron Willard BOSTON"; lower case panel is centered by an inlaid urn, ogee bracket feet, the upper case is crested by a pierced fretwork centered by brass urn finial, mellow ruddy patina. Made by Aaron Willard, Boston, Massachusetts, circa 1780-1790.

According to family documents, this was the parlor clock of Governor James Sullivan (1744-1808), delegate to Continental Congress, Governor of Massachusetts in 1807-1808. Governor Sullivan owned the clock from 1784-1808.

Ht. 36″ Wd. 14¼″ Dp. 6½″

P4273 Hepplewhite mahogany three part dining table consisting of a dropleaf center section and two semi-circular ends; the aprons and legs with inlaid borders; the top features fine figured mahogany with a mellow brown patina. Massachusetts circa 1780-1800.

Ht. 37½″

62½″ closed Wd. 47½″

P4298 Hepplewhite mahogany upholstered back side chair; tapered legs with serpentine corner brackets; serpentine seat with bowed sides and bowed crest rail; the chair retains the original linen undercover. Massachusetts circa 1790-1800.
An identical chair, apparently of the same set, is in the Henry F. du Pont Winterthur Museum (Montgomery "Federal Furniture" plate 44).

Ht. 37½″

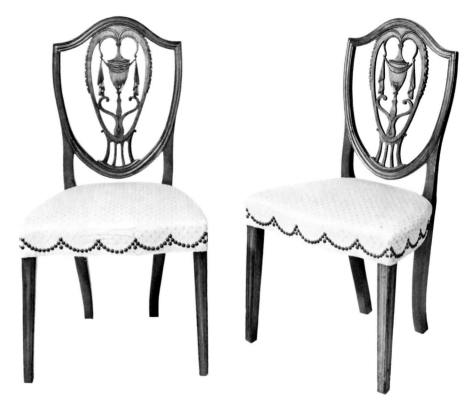

P4218 Pair of Hepplewhite mahogany shield back side chairs; the splat is a study in beauty and creativity with a central urn and drapery supported at the base by serpentine scrolls and held from the top by scrolled vines, the whole contained in an oval frame with bellflower carved edges; tapered moulded legs; golden patina. Salem, Massachusetts, or Connecticut circa 1780-1800. In mint original condition.

Ex-collection Mr. and Mrs. Mitchel Taradash.

These chairs are of the same design, but not of the set, as the set of six dining chairs formerly in the Taradash collection, illustrated ANTIQUES and now in our collection. They stand among the finest and most beautiful examples of American Hepplewhite chairs.

Ht. 39″

P4221 Hepplewhite mahogany and gilt mirror with gilded original urn and side leaves; carved and gilded inner border and swan neck pediment with carved rosettes. New York circa 1780-1810.

Ht. 52″ Wd. 22″

P4268 Watercolor depiction of Mount Vernon in contemporary gilt frame with spiral border. New England circa 1800-1820.

Ht. 19½″ Wd. 23½″

P4249 Classical mahogany sofa; three panelled carved back; the center panel cornucopia flanked by two drapery carved panels; serpentine wings with reeded facades continuing along seat frame; outsplayed reeded legs ending in claw casters. Attributed to Duncan Phyfe, New York circa 1810-1820. Fine mellow patina and with carving of first quality.

Ht. 33″ Lg. 6′9½″

P3999 Sheraton mahogany dropleaf dining table;
the pedestal is formed of a cylindrical column
with alternating reeding; four outsplayed legs
with moulded surface ending in brass casters; the
top is rectangular with rounded corners and is
distinguished by superbly figured mahogany with
a beautiful golden patina. Attributed to Duncan
Phyfe, New York, circa 1810-1820.

Ht. 29¼″ Lg. 60¼″ open Wd. 48″
　　　　　27″ closed

P4251 Rare Sheraton mahogany work table; circular top and case with two rows of drawers, the
two small drawers swivel on fulcrums; the ring
roundel with chased brass center rosette is lifted
by three arched supports emanating from the
base of the ring turned tapered legs; brass paw
casters. Boston or Salem, Massachusetts, circa
1810-1820.
Related examples are in the Essex Institute "19th
Century America Exhibit" catalogue No. 13 and
also "Furniture of the Olden Time" by Frances
Clara Morse, illus. 265.

Ht. 29½″ Diam. 18¼″

P4277 Chippendale walnut tripod tilt top candlestand with circular dish top; ball and ring turned column with nicely tapered shaft; cabriole legs ending in bulbous pad feet; mellow light brown patina. Philadelphia circa 1760-1780.

The low height of this stand makes it more suitable than most as an occasional table.

Ht. 25½″ Diam. 23½″

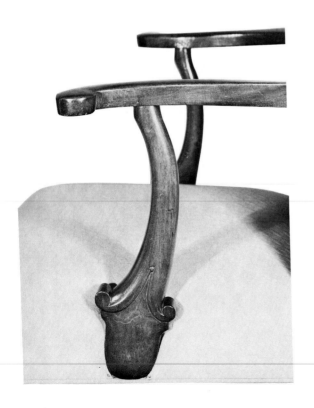

P4284 Chippendale mahogany Martha Washington armchair or lolling chair; the arm supports with scrolled voluted base and the serpentine arms with scrolled terminals are characteristic of Newburyport handiwork; this example is fashioned of dense close grained San Domingan mahogany. Newburyport, Massachusetts, circa 1760-1780.

Ht. 43″ Wd. 28″

P2922 Chippendale San Domingan dropleaf table; square top with deeply moulded edge; finely modelled cabriole legs with pointed knees; sculptured claw and ball feet and cyma scrolled apron. Boston, Massachusetts, circa 1760-1780.
Purchased from descendants of the Porter family of Boston.

Ht. 27″ Lg. 42″ Wd. 15½″ closed
41½″ open

P4275 Pair of leather decorated fire buckets inscribed "Will'm Donnison 1782"; bearing the motto "Impavida Flammarus" each is branded "Fenno." Made by I. Fenno, leather maker, Boston, Massachusetts, 1782.
The buckets each contain linen carrying bags for silver, stencilled Joseph Belknap 1792 and John Lovett 1799.

Ht. 19″ (including original handles) Diam. 9″

P4279 Mahogany pipe box with finely scrolled sides, partitions and cresting and with the rare feature of a divided scrolled partition; one drawer; the detailed workmanship and fine dovetails show the handiwork of a competent craftsman rather than an itinerant; mellow brown patina. Newport, Rhode Island, circa 1750-1760.

Ht. 20″ Wd. 6½″ Dp. 5″

P4297 William and Mary maple rush seat side chair with Prince of Wales carved crest; finely turned base and stretchers and ball feet; the moulded banisters are a rare variation. Massachusetts circa 1710-1730.

Ht. 47¼″

P4209 Pilgrim maple and pine small oval top trestle base table; fine ball and ring turned columns supported on trestle bases with horizontal braces; oval pine top; fine old color. Massachusetts circa 1680-1710. Ex-collection Mr. and Mrs. Mitchel Taradash.

Ht. 26½″ Top 28¾″ x 17½″

P4214 Pennsylvania German Open dresser, made of long leaf pine and retaining the original blue green decoration; the panelled doors of the base have painted flower pots with tulips and daisies and the date "ANNO 1787." The sides of the upper case are finely scalloped while the scalloping of the crest board complements that of the base. Pennsylvania circa 1787. To our knowledge this is the only scalloped dresser with Pennsylvania German decoration.

Ex-collection Mr. and Mrs. Mitchel Taradash.

Illustrated "LIVING WITH ANTIQUES" Winchester, page 90.

Ht. 83″ Lg. 62″ Dp. 18″

P4205 Profile silhouette depicting George Turner, Esq., Attorney at Law, signed "Sam'l Metford, Fecit." Newport, Rhode Island. In original bird's eye maple frame. Samuel Metford (1810-1896) specialized in silhouetted profiles. He worked in various Northern cities, also Charleston, S. C., and returned to England in 1844.

Ht. 13″ Wd. 10″

P4226 Chippendale walnut slant top desk of rare small size, fluted quarter columns; ogee bracket feet; fine interior with double row of serpentine blocked drawers, fluted document drawers and crotch figured center door, the pigeonhole terminals conceal small drawers; mellow light brown patina. Pennsylvania circa 1750-1780.

Ht. 45½″ Wd. 36″ Dp. 22″ Wg. Lvl. 32½″

P4258 Chippendale cherry tripod candlestand, square top with raised beaded border, slender tapering column with elliptical ball base, graceful cabriole legs with ridged surface; the top is centered by an inlaid star motif, beautiful amber color. Massachusetts circa 1780-1800.

Ht. 28½″ Top 17″ x 16¾″

P4271 Queen Anne maple wing chair; the finely modelled cabriole legs have ankles set forward into the pad in the Newport manner; the rare maple legs and stretchers are enhanced by a golden patina. Newport, Rhode Island, circa 1750-1760. The chair was purchased from the Brown family. The appearance of a chair of this refinement in maple is rare.

Ht. 47½″ Wd. 35″ Dp. 30″

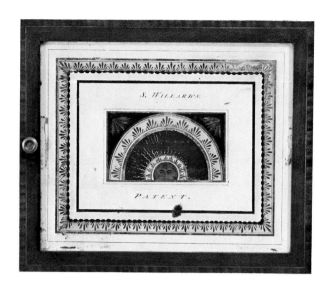

P4270 Banjo clock with original eglomise glass panels in crossbanded mahogany frames; the base panel inscribed "S. Willard's Patent"; the waist panel with gilt urn and floral center; both glasses with white background and blue borders; the dial has the typical gilded outer border. Made by Simon Willard, Roxbury, Massachusetts, circa 1802-1815.

Ht. 34″ Wd. 9⅝″ Dp. 3½″

P4274 Sheraton gilt mirror; the eglomise panel features an engraved vignette of Washington in a border of 16 stars and flanked by a laurel wreath; original gilt and glass. Philadelphia circa 1800-1815.

Ht. 37″ Wd. 17″

P4294 Queen Anne flat top highboy; the fronts are San Domingan mahogany and the sides and legs maple; the majority of the engraved bat wing brasses secured by cotter pins are original; the replacement brasses are of the period; the crusty old finish has been left undisturbed and displays great character and authentic aspect. Salem, Massachusetts, or vicinity circa 1740-1750.

Ht. 6′ Wd. 37½″ Dp. 21″

P4216 Classical mahogany accordion dining table; the basic unit contains three pedestals each with scrolled supports; serpentine outsplayed legs with acanthus carving, reeding and brass claw casters; the end sections each support drop leaves and the accordion arrangement which extends to receive four original leaves; fine condition and color. Philadelphia circa 1810-1820. The table descended in the Stockton family of Princeton.
Ex-collection Mr. and Mrs. Mitchel Taradash.
Illustrated ANTIQUES January, 1953 pg. 46.

Ht. 28½" Wd. 66" Lg. 50½" closed 12'10" fully extended

CCORDION DINING TABLE

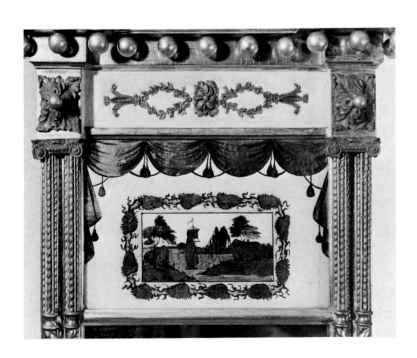

P4296 Sheraton gilt mirror with double spiral columns with Corinthian capitals supporting a decorated frieze with off-white background; the eglomise panel is of exceptional quality with marine scene bordered by draped curtains and tassels; original gilt and glass. New England circa 1810-1820.

Ht. 44½″ Wd. 25¼″

P4255 Sheraton mahogany small ladies secretary; the desk compartment is in the form of a lap desk with crossbanded and inlaid borders and one drawer below; the glass doors with narrow gothic mullions enclose an interior of drawers, pigeonholes and shelves; slender reeded legs. Portsmouth, New Hampshire, circa 1800-1810.

Ht. 5′4¼″ Wd. 31″ Dp. 20″
Wrtg. Lvl. 31¼″

P4272 Hepplewhite mahogany side table; rectangular case with two divided drawers; tapered legs; mellow brown patina. New York circa 1780-1800.

Ht. 29″ Wd. 35″ Dp. 20½″

P4253 William and Mary walnut library table of important size and rare quality; the case contains two large and one small drawer; superb ball and ring turnings ending in ball feet; the square side stretchers have moulded edges, the medial stretcher has moulded canted sides; the top is fashioned of two boards with cleated ends and is hinged with shaped cleats abutting the sides; original mellow patina. Pennsylvania circa 1720-1740. Purchased from the family of Luke Vincent Lockwood. Illustrated in Lockwood "Colonial Furniture in America," enlarged edition 1921, Vol. II, Fig. 676.

Ht. 29¾″ Lg. 6′7½″ Dp. 30¾″

THE TARADASH COLLECTION
(Continued)

Chippendale mahogany blockfront bureau, Massachusetts circa 1760-1780. Illustrated "American Antiques from Israel Sack Collection" Vol. IV, page 863, and Vol. VI, page 20.

Chippendale mahogany ball and claw foot lowboy, Philadelphia circa 1760-1780. Illustrated "American Antiques from Israel Sack Collection" Vol. VI, page 1594. Private collection.

Queen Anne walnut side chair, Philadelphia circa 1750-1760. Illustrated "Living With Antiques" Alice Winchester, page 91. Private collection.

Chippendale ball and claw foot upholstered armchair, Newport, Rhode Island, circa 1760-1770. Ex-collection Dwight Blaney, pioneer collector. Illustrated "Colonial Furniture in America" Lockwood, Vol. II, fig. 582. Illustrated "Arts and Crafts of Newport" Ralph Carpenter, plate 25. Private collection.

felt that since Israel Sack built the collection which had become so valuable that we should have the opportunity to acquire most of what she disposed of as long as we were able. That we met the challenge is apparent in the following illustrations of objects we acquired from the Taradash collection. Most have been illustrated in Volumes IV, V and VI and will be so designated under the illustrations. But

we felt that by showing all the objects acquired by us from the Taradash collection even in capsule size would give an idea of the magnificence of the collection. It will also serve to pay a tribute to two exceptional people who demanded, lived and loved the most brilliant expressions of American artistic achievements and to Israel Sack who made the light shine brighter.

continued on page 1311

Ball and claw foot mahogany inlaid serpentine front bureau, Newport, Rhode Island, circa 1780-1800. Illustrated ANTIQUES December 1946, page 394. Illustrated "Arts and Crafts of Newport" Ralph Carpenter, page 61. Illustrated "American Antiques from Israel Sack Collection" Vol. V, page 1127 and 1277. Private collection.

Sheraton mahogany and satinwood sewing table, attributed to John Seymour, Boston, Massachusetts, circa 1800-1810. Illustrated ANTIQUES June 1946, page 360. Illustrated "American Antiques from Israel Sack Collection" Vol. IV, page 867 and 1007. Private collection.

Sheraton mahogany sewing table, attributed to William Hook, Salem, Massachusetts, circa 1800-1810. Illustrated "American Antiques from Israel Sack Collection" page 1074, Vol. IV. Private collection.

Pair Chippendale mahogany card tables, attributed to John Townsend, Newport, Rhode Island, circa 1760-1780. Illustrated "American Antiques from Israel Sack Collection" Vol. II, page 555. Illustrated "Arts and Crafts of Newport," Ralph Carpenter, page 95. Illustrated ANTIQUES January 1953, page 46. Private collection.

continued on page 1388

In 1935 the late Charles K. Davis walked into our shop at 422 Madison Avenue and introduced himself. He stated that after purchasing a copy of Wallace Nutting's "Furniture Treasury" the illustrations under the Sack captions appealed to him, and he thought it advisable to make our acquaintance as he intended to furnish his new home in Fairfield, Connecticut, where he had been transferred by the du Pont Company and made President of the newly acquired Remington Arms Co.

A friendship developed which lasted throughout these 40 odd years and involved both families. We feel that this type of relationship which is based on mutual respect and admiration is similar to the relationship that no doubt developed between many of our country's artist crafstmen and their patrons. For this type of service an extra ingredient is added—difficult to measure but so evident in the result.

The January and March 1941 issues of ANTIQUES featured two articles on the Davis collection. All the antique American furniture with only a few isolated exceptions was purchased from Israel Sack, Inc. The collection was enhanced by several great examples of American colonial silver and pewter chiefly under the aegis of Charles Montgomery who was introduced to C. K. Davis by Harold Sack. Mr. Davis's philosophy was fundamental. Seek out the top expert in a field and go with him all the way.

Connoisseurs and students have long known the reputation of this collection. At his death a few pieces by instruction were sold to Winterthur—the Frothingham matching highboy and lowboy, the William and Mary ball foot veneered desk, the Curtis girandole clock and the famous and unique John Burt silver pair of candlesticks, snuffer and tray acquired from Hermann Clarke of Boston by our firm. At this time our company repurchased the William and Mary burl walnut octagonal slate top dressing table now on loan to the Museum of Fine Arts, Boston, by the Dietrich Brothers Americana Foundation, the Hermann Clarke blockfront kneehole desk, a Gaines armchair, and the choice Queen Anne Massachusetts tea table with drawer.

The remainder of the collection was left to his wife, Bertha B. Davis, and it is on her recent demise that the rest of the collection became available.

Studded with pieces of top quality, they all reflect the sense of quality and proportion which thread is evident throughout the entire collection.

It is interesting to note that the vast preponderance of the major items were repurchased by our firm.

While this brochure is offering a wide variety of quality pieces, we thought it fitting and more meaningful to segregate the Davis pieces to give a clearer idea of their importance as a unit.

The Davis Collection

P4344 Queen Anne walnut corner chair with four cabriole legs ending in claw and ball feet; block and arrow turned cross stretchers; horseshoe seat; the front leg with shell and bellflower carving on knee and cyma knee brackets; violin splats; mellow medium brown patina. Newport, Rhode Island, circa 1740-1760. One of the finest New England corner chairs we have had the privilege to own.
Ex-collection Israel Sack, Inc. May 1939.
Ex-collection Charles K. Davis.
Illustrated ANTIQUES March 1941, page 127.

Ht. 31¾″ Wd. 29″

P4374 Chippendale cherry block front desk; three blocked case drawers; the upper drawer with three shells; ogee bracket feet; superb amphitheatre interior, the amphitheatre formed by banks of cyma shaped drawers capped with scooped pigeonhole drawers and centered by fan carved center row of drawers; fine old color. Connecticut circa 1760-1780.

From the family of Moses Paige, Hartford, Connecticut.

Exhibited Rhode Island School of Design.

Ex-collection Israel Sack, Inc.

Ex-collection Charles K. Davis.

Illustrated ANTIQUES January 1941, page 20.

Ht. 45¼″ Wd. 42″ Dp. 27″ Wr. Ht. 32¼″

The Davis Collection

P4351 Chippendale San Domingan mahogany small card table; the front and sides are serpentine in shape and blocked from the solid; the aprons are serpentine in the reverse plane with carved borders; the conforming top has a border of repeat fluted notches; the reeding of the stop fluting extends half way up the legs which retain the original casters; the pierced corner brackets are the original and a drawer is concealed by the rear gate; the condition and patina of this gem is superb; the top has a swirling grain with a flowing bronze patina of rare beauty. Attributed to John Townsend, Newport, Rhode Island, circa 1770-1790.
Ex-collection Israel Sack, Inc. 1940.
Ex-collection Charles K. Davis.

Ht. 27¼″ Wd. 29¾″ Dp. 14½″

The Davis Collection

P4352 Rare small Chippendale mahogany tripod candlestand with piecrust top; spiral urn column with tapering shaft and maple block to support the tilting top; ovoid claw and ball feet; old or original finish. Massachusetts circa 1760-1780.
Exhibited at Fogg Art Museum, Cambridge, Massachusetts, 1933.
Ex-collection Israel Sack, Inc. 1940.
Ex-collection Charles K. Davis.
Illustrated ANTIQUES January 1941, page 21.

Ht. 27¼″ Diam. 20¼″

The Davis Collection

P4353 Hepplewhite mahogany tall clock by Aaron Willard, Boston, and bearing the original directions for setting up the clock engraved by Paul Revere; the case has finely figured grained fronts of waist and base with cross banded borders; French feet; original beautifully scrolled fretwork and brass finials; the dial and door are exceptional and unique; the concave dished dial has a domed panel above painted in gilt on a white background "Aaron Willard, Washington St., Boston"; the glass door features an eglomise landscape in pastel colors with eglomise floral spandrels in the corners flanking the dished dial; behind the works on the inside of the backboard is the contemporary chalk inscription "A. Willard"; old or original finish. Made by Aaron Willard, Boston, Massachusetts, circa 1800-1820.
Exhibited in Fogg Art Museum 1933.
Ex-collection Israel Sack, Inc. 1937.
Ex-collection Charles K. Davis.
Illustrated ANTIQUES January 1941, page 20.

Ht. 8'4¼" Wd. 19" Dp. 9½"

P4349 Queen Anne walnut armchair; tall slender proportion with round stiles and blocked members to receive the sinuous serpentine arms; the cyma shaped flat medial stretcher is joined by turned side stretchers; the front and side aprons are cyma shaped, the side profile is boldly spooned; the finish is old or original. Newport, Rhode Island, circa 1730-1750.

With the exception of a flat stretcher armchair in the Henry F. du Pont Winterthur Museum, we know of no other example in any museum collection and only one or possibly two examples in private collections.

Ex-collection Israel Sack, Inc. 1939.

Ex-collection Charles K. Davis.

Illustrated ANTIQUES March 1941, page 128.

Ht. 42½″ Wd. 31″

The Davis Collection

P4342 Queen Anne walnut low back upholstered armchair; compass or horseshoe shaped upholstered seat; cabriole legs with broad rounded knees to conform to the broad curve of the seat frame; bold serpentine bend to the cabriole legs and pad feet; serpentine arms with broad scooped arm rests and scrolled terminals; the arm supports serpentine with an S bend under the arm; upholstered back of bowed outline; original finish; cherry framework. New York circa 1740-1760.

American low upholstered armchairs are quite rare, this New York Queen Anne form being the finest known. A related example also from the Tibbits family is in Winterthur, Downs #17, and another is in the Metropolitan Museum of Art.

Descended in the Tibbits family of Hoosick Falls, New York.

Ex-collection Israel Sack, Inc. 1939.

Ex-collection Charles K. Davis.

Illustrated ANTIQUES January 1941, page 19.

Ht. 35¾" Dp. 26¾"

The Davis Collection

P4350 Chippendale walnut blockfront bureau; the square blocking adds boldness to the compact form; original bat wing brasses of Queen Anne influence; bracket feet; the deep nut brown original patina is of great depth and mellowness. Massachusetts circa 1750-1770.
Ex-collection Israel Sack, Inc. 1938.
Ex-collection Charles K. Davis.
Illustrated "Fine Points of Furniture, Early American", page 185.

Ht. 30½" Wd. 35½" Dp. 20¼"

The Davis Collection

P4355 Queen Anne walnut bonnet top highboy; boldly carved fan in top and bottom sections; the cabriole legs with platformed pad feet are removable, a feature typical in Newport but rare in Massachusetts; superb state of preservation with a beautiful bronze patina; retains original brass handles with spurred bales and the central flame finial. Salem, Massachusetts, circa 1750-1760.
Ex-collection Israel Sack, Inc. 1939.
Ex-collection Charles K. Davis.
Illustrated "Fine Points of Furniture, Early American", page 185.

Ht. 7'4¼" Wd. 37¾" Dp. 21"

The Davis Collection

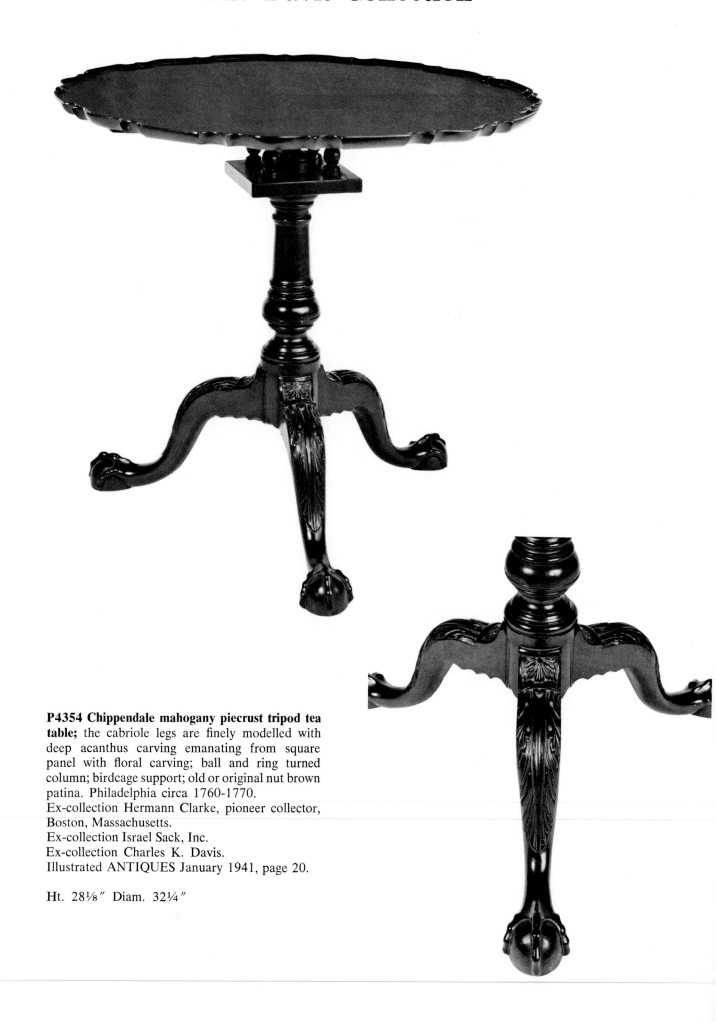

P4354 Chippendale mahogany piecrust tripod tea table; the cabriole legs are finely modelled with deep acanthus carving emanating from square panel with floral carving; ball and ring turned column; birdcage support; old or original nut brown patina. Philadelphia circa 1760-1770.
Ex-collection Hermann Clarke, pioneer collector, Boston, Massachusetts.
Ex-collection Israel Sack, Inc.
Ex-collection Charles K. Davis.
Illustrated ANTIQUES January 1941, page 20.

Ht. 28⅛″ Diam. 32¼″

The Davis Collection

P4364 Chippendale slant top desk; San Domingan mahogany with plum pudding figure; ogee bracket feet; original bale brasses; the blockfront interior is indicative of the work of John Townsend or a related Townsend; the center door has a fully developed carved shell with fluted center; the end drawers have wavy shells with scribed borders; the scooped pigeonhole terminal drawers and the neat dovetails are identical to those on labelled Townsend interiors; old dark finish. Attributed to John Townsend or a member of the Townsend family of master craftsmen, Newport, Rhode Island, circa 1750-1770.
Formerly in the Frederick Williamson family of Montclair, New Jersey.
Ex-collection Israel Sack, Inc. 1940.
Ex-collection Charles K. Davis.
Illustrated ANTIQUES March 1941, page 128.

Ht. 42¼″ Wd. 40″ Dp. 24″ Writing Level 31″

The Davis Collection

P4331 Mahogany banjo clock with original eglomise glass panels in door and waist framed by crossbanded borders; gilded bracket below and gilded acorn finial; delicately wrought brass side arms; enamel dial in fine state and original T-bridge escapement brass movement, also retaining the original pendulum, weight and winding key; the painted panels are superb rivalling the finest examples known, the base panel depicts crossed flags, banners and drums closely related to the painting of the Declaration of Independence by John Trumbull included in the recent exhibit "The Eye of Thomas Jefferson" in The National Gallery of Art in Washington; the waist panel depicts a gilt allegoric figure of Justice in white background; both panels have broad etched gilt borders and white outer borders; both panels are secured by the original thin rods with original needle thin nails and the pastel back surfaces have never been varnished over; the iron pendulum plate behind the door panel bears the original inscription "E. Taber, Roxbury, Massachusetts." Made by Elnathan Taber, Roxbury, Massachusetts, circa 1810-1820.
Purchased from Professor Fisher of Yale University.
Ex-collection Israel Sack, Inc. July 1939.
Ex-collection Charles K. Davis.
Illustrated ANTIQUES March 1941, page 128.

Ht. 39½" Wd. 10" Dp. 3¾"

P4340 Sheraton mahogany octagonal shaped sewing table with flame satinwood veneered case; the front with one drawer and sewing slide retaining the original brass knobs; tapering reeded legs ending in bulbous feet; the top is centered by an oval of satinwood and the borders of the top and apron are crossbanded; the table retains the original finish. Salem, Massachusetts, circa 1800-1810.
Ex-collection Israel Sack, Inc. 1939.
Ex-collection Charles K. Davis.

Ht. 29½″ Wd. 20½″ Dp. 15¾″

The Davis Collection

P3283 Queen Anne mahogany rectangular tea table; applied concave moulded tray top with notched corners; cyma scrolled bulged apron borders; tall slender cabriole legs ending in platformed pad feet; the drawer in one end retaining the original early tear drop brass handle is, to our knowledge, a unique feature; the table is in the original undisturbed state with the original finish; supporting brace for the drawer and the pine glue blocks virtually intact. Massachusetts circa 1730-1740.

Ex-collection Israel Sack, Inc. 1939.
Ex-collection Charles K. Davis.
Illustrated ANTIQUES January 1941, page 19.
Illustrated "Fine Points of Furniture, Early American" page 247.

Ht. 27¼″ Lg. 31½″ Wd. 19½″

The Davis Collection

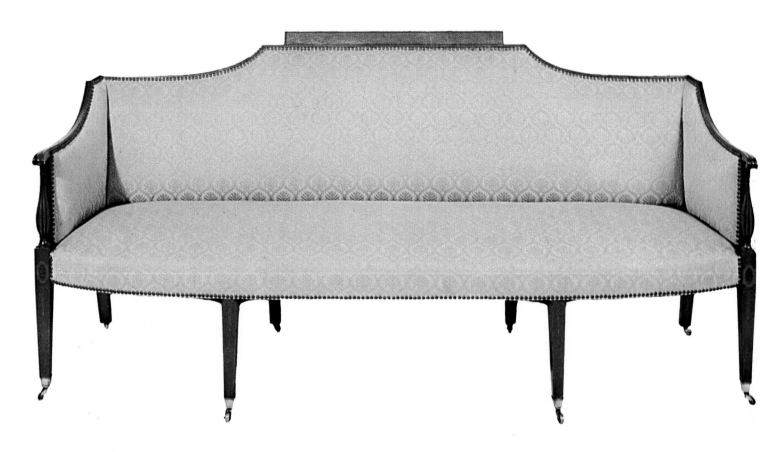

P4356 Hepplewhite mahogany sofa; the crest with central satinwood panel supported by arched wings; the arms terminate in knuckle carved terminals with bulbous reeded arm supports; the tapered legs are inlaid with a loop or chain pattern and end in brass claw casters; the plinths above are fronted by paterae of contrasting wood with cut corners; mellow finish. Baltimore or Annapolis, Maryland, circa 1780-1800.

This sofa descended in the Mason family of Washingington, D. C.

Ex-collection Israel Sack, Inc. 1937.

Ex-collection Charles K. Davis.

Illustrated ANTIQUES Frontispiece March 1940 and captioned "Masterpieces of American Furniture in Private Collections."

Illustrated "Fine Points of Furniture, Early American" page 228.

Ht. 38¼″ Lg. 82½″ Dp. 30½″

The Davis Collection

P4336 Queen Anne walnut wing chair; beautifully modelled cabriole legs with platformed pad feet; turned stretchers; serpentine crest rails; the seat frame is horseshoe shaped which lends fluency to the lines not usually seen in the serpentine crested group; maple frame; "S.G." burned in frame; original mellow patina. Massachusetts circa 1740-1760.
Ex-collection Israel Sack, Inc. 1938.
Ex-collection Charles K. Davis.
Illustrated ANTIQUES January 1941, pages 19 and 21.

Ht. 46″ Wd. 35″ Dp. 31″

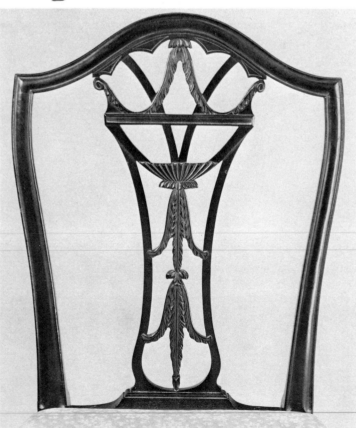

P4347 Pair of Hepplewhite mahogany side chairs; the back with bowed moulded stiles and splat supported on a shoe base is transitional in form; the splat is superbly carved featuring the elliptical urn and drapery in oval frame as seen in the more prevalent Rhode Island shield back group; this element is supported by a bent frame that enclosed two large carved bellflowers; tapered moulded legs; fine dark color. Rhode Island circa 1790-1800.

Ex-collection Israel Sack, Inc. 1939.

Ex-collection Charles K. Davis.

A chair of this pattern (or of this set) was given by Charles K. Davis to the Henry F. du Pont Winterthur Museum. The Winterthur chair is illustrated in Montgomery "Federal Furniture" plate 42.

Ht. 39″

P4375 Hepplewhite mahogany secretary; the upper case with Gothic doors formed by reeded mullions supported on inlaid plinths; below the glass doors which retain the original wavy glass panes are two rows of small drawers with inlaid borders; the cornice has a crossbanded center panel and reeded plinths supporting the original brass finials; four drawers in base with a checkered inlaid base and French feet; choice mellow brown patina. Massachusetts circa 1780-1800. From the Barton family of Newburyport, Massachusetts.
Ex-collection Israel Sack, Inc. 1938.
Ex-collection Charles K. Davis.

Ht. 75¾″ Wd. 44½″ Dp. 20″

The Davis Collection

P4361 Hepplewhite mahogany four drawer tambour desk; the drawer fronts and center door are fronted by flame satinwood veneer; the door is flanked by tambours enclosing pigeon-hole compartments and drawers; the oval brasses are the original; French feet; the piece exhibits a rare deep brown patina of great depth and mellowness. Massachusetts circa 1780-1800.

Ex-collection Hermann Clarke.

Ex-collection Israel Sack, Inc. 1941.

Ex-collection Charles K. Davis.

Note: Hermann Clarke was one of the most discriminating collectors of the Boston area in the 1920's. Every piece in his collection was the finest as exemplified by this example, the Philadelphia piecrust table #P4354 in the brochure, etc. He was the owner of the unique silver candlesticks, snuffer and tray combination. Harold Sack bought this from him in 1941. Mr. Clarke sold them because he was sure the country was going to seed because of the staggering national debt. The set was sold to Mr. Charles K. Davis and is now in Winterthur.

Ht. 46½″ Wt. 37″ Dp. 30¾″

The Davis Collection

P4383 Chippendale mahogany claw and ball foot bed; the claw and ball feet of the footposts have swept back talons and knobby knuckles of Boston design; the carved knee caps have acanthus and cartouche carving in stippled background; the octagonal head posts and rails are birch; the arched headboard pine. Boston or Charlestown, Massachusetts, circa 1760-1780.
From the family of Mrs. Guy Strickler, Providence, Rhode Island.
Ex-collection Israel Sack, Inc. 1938.
Ex-collection Charles K. Davis.
Illustrated ANTIQUES March 1941, page 128.

Ht. 83″ Lg. 6′4″ Wd. 54″

The Davis Collection

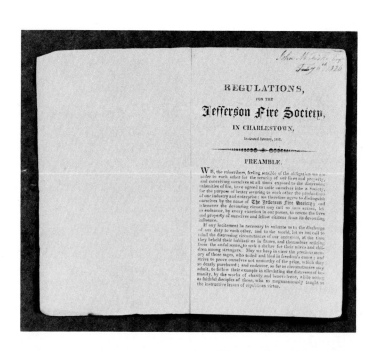

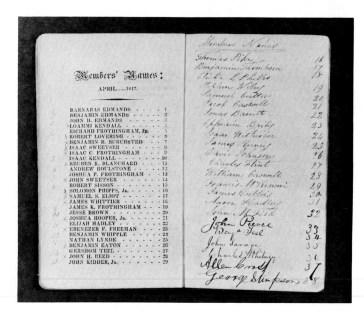

P4371 Leather decorated fire bucket featuring a large spread eagle grasping arrows and olive branch and the banner "Jefferson Fire Society, John M. Fiske 1826" and on reverse "Charlestown." Accompanying the bucket is the register of the Society with John M. Fisk(e) listed as member #32. Ex-collection Charles K. Davis.

Ht. 19", Diameter 8½"

The Davis Collection

P4346 Chippendale mahogany ball and claw foot side chair; the splat is centered by tassel and ruffle carving; acanthus carved crest and knees; gadrooned moulding and squared claw and ball feet; retaining the old or original finish. New York circa 1760-1780. Chairs of this form were made for the Van Rensselaer family and other prominent New York families. This chair was part of the original purchase by Charles K. Davis from Israel Sack, Inc., on May 20, 1936.

Ex-collection Israel Sack, Inc. 1936.
Ex-collection Charles K. Davis.
Illustrated ANTIQUES January 1941, page 21.

Ht. 38½"

The Davis Collection

P4376 Sheraton mahogany secretary of rare small size and beautiful proportion; the base contains one drawer with original chased brass knobs; the case is supported on tall graceful bulbous reeded legs; choice bronze patina. Massachusetts circa 1800-1810.
Ex-collection Israel Sack, Inc.
Ex-collection Charles K. Davis.

Ht. 72½″ Wd. 36″ Dp. 21″

The Davis Collection

P4368 Chippendale mahogany chest-on-chest; claw and ball feet of squared New York outline in front; ogee bracket feet in rear, gadrooned moulding in base; the upper and lower case sections have chamfered fluted corners; original brasses and mellow brown patina. Attributed to Thomas Burling, New York circa 1760-1770. This chest descended in the family of Benjamin Wynkoop, early New York silversmith. It is illustrated in ANTIQUES Magazine, May 1936, relating it to a labelled desk by Thomas Burling. At that time, it was in the possession of Mrs. Albert Wynkoop, a direct descendant of the silversmith.
Ex-collection Mrs. Albert W. Wynkoop.
Ex-collection Israel Sack, Inc. 1936.
Ex-collection Charles K. Davis.
Illustrated ANTIQUES January 1941, page 21.

Ht. 78¾″ Wd. 48″ Dp. 22½″

The Davis Collection

P4372 Hepplewhite mahogany serpentine front sideboard with recessed center compartment flanked by bowed turrets; the doors have circular panels with inlaid borders while the turrets have similar oval panels; the tapered legs are fronted by chain inlay; the center legs are canted to conform to the serpentine outline; choice mellow brown patina. New York circa 1780-1800.
Ex-collection Israel Sack, Inc. 1937.
Ex-collection Charles K. Davis.
Illustrated ANTIQUES March 1941, page 126.

Ht. 43" Lg. 72½" Dp. 27¼"

The Davis Collection

P4338 Pair of satinwood knife boxes with shield shaped silver escutcheon mounts and the original fitted interiors; the fronts of each are serpentine shaped with concave centers and fronted by inlaid columns; shell inlaid lids; the patina is of great depth and mellowness. English circa 1780-1800.
Ex-collection Israel Sack, Inc.
Ex-collection Charles K. Davis.

Ht. 15¼″ Wd. 8⅜″ Dp. 10¾″

P4365 Sheraton mahogany sofa; bowed back and seat; reeded arms and bulbous reeded arm supports; bulbous turned legs with flame satinwood panels flanking the seat; fine mellow patina. Salem, Massachusetts, circa 1800-1810.
Ex-collection Israel Sack, Inc. 1937.
Ex-collection Charles K. Davis.
Illustrated ANTIQUES January 1941, page 18.

Ht. 37½″ Wd. 6′ Dp. 24½″

The Davis Collection

P4395 Classical mahogany dropleaf library table with clover leaf shaped leaves; drawer in one end; a reeded urn column with carved base moulding is supported on four out-splayed legs with acanthus carved and reeded legs; fine golden patina; school of Duncan Phyfe. New York circa 1810-1820.
Ex-collection Israel Sack, Inc. 1941
Ex-collection Charles K. Davis

Ht. 29½"Lg. 37½"
Wd. Closed 26¼"—Open 51¼"

P4343 Sheraton mahogany armchair; the crest with ribbon and bowknot carved panel; double cross bar splats with rosette carved centers; bowed serpentine arms with reeded facade; urn shaped turned arm supports, the urns acanthus carved; bell shaped seat with reeded facade; reeded legs with bulbous feet; old or original finish. Attributed to Duncan Phyfe, New York circa 1800-1810.
Ex-collection Israel Sack, Inc. 1938.
Ex-collection Charles K. Davis.

Ht. 32¼" Wd. 21½"

The Davis Collection

P4359 Chippendale mahogany card table; cabriole legs with claw and ball feet; one drawer; gadrooned apron moulding; old or original finish. Philadelphia circa 1760-1780.
From the Sloan family of Philadelphia.
Ex-collection Israel Sack, Inc. 1936.
Ex-collection Charles K. Davis.

Ht. 28¾″ Wd. 36″ Dp. 17¾″

P4334 Hepplewhite mahogany pembroke table; oval top with line inlaid borders; conforming case with drawer at one end; the tapered legs with pyramidal inlay; columnal inlaid plinths above; beautiful mellow brown patina. Newport, Rhode Island, circa 1780-1800.
Ex-collection Israel Sack, Inc. 1937
Ex-collection Charles K. Davis.

Ht. 25⅝″ Lg. 30¾″
Wd. 38½″ Open—19¾″ Closed

The Davis Collection

P4360 Sheraton mahogany armchair; square back; the splat finely curved with drapery and plume motifs and framed in arch with fan carved spandrels; serpentine arms ending in carved rosettes; reeded legs with spade feet; fine old or original patina. New York circa 1800.
Ex-collection Israel Sack, Inc. 1938.
Ex-collection Charles K. Davis.
Illustrated ANTIQUES March 1941, page 127.

Ht. 34½″ Wd. 23″

P4341 Sheraton mahogany serving or dressing table of rare small size; serpentine front; one drawer with original knobs; turret corners; conforming top with reeded edge; bulbous reeded legs; brass casters; original finish. Massachusetts circa 1800-1810.
Ex-collection Israel Sack, Inc.
Ex-collection Charles K. Davis.

Ht. 33½″ Wd. 28″ Dp. 16½″

The Davis Collection

P4363 Hepplewhite mahogany demilune card table; the tapered legs are inlaid with typical Baltimore bellflowers ending in spade feet; the plinths with oval inlaid leaf paterae; the legs and frame have checkered inlaid borders and the top has a concave moulded edge; choice bronze patina. Baltimore or Annapolis, Maryland, circa 1780-1800.
Ex-collection Israel Sack, Inc. 1939.
Ex-collection Charles K. Davis.

Ht. 29⅛" Wd. 36" Dp. 17¾"

P4345 Hepplewhite mahogany shield back side chair; superbly carved splat with drapery and bellflower center; tapering reeded legs and spade feet; the chair is notable for its stately proportion; crisp carving and superb original condition including finish. New York circa 1790-1800.
Ex-collection Israel Sack, Inc. 1939.
Ex-collection Charles K. Davis.

Ht. 38¼"

The Davis Collection

P4348 Pair of Chippendale mahogany claw and ball foot side chairs; the splats are centered by tassel and ruffle carving; acanthus carved crests and knees; gadrooned mouldings; squared claw and ball feet; fine bronze patina. New York circa 1760-1780. Chairs of this form were made for the Van Rensselaer family and other prominent New York families.
Ex-collection Israel Sack, Inc. 1936.
Ex-collection Charles K. Davis.

Ht. 38½″

The Davis Collection

P4366 Hepplewhite mahogany washstand; flat shape cross stretcher with dish rim; slightly tapered legs ending in Marlborough feet; one drawer. Massachusetts circa 1780-1800.
Ex-collection Israel Sack, Inc. 1939.
Ex-collection Charles K. Davis.

Ht. 32¾″ Wd. 13″ Dp. 13″

P4337 Queen Anne maple wing chair of rare small scale; the seat frame was designed to be partly exposed as it is now upholstered; pointed knees; bold curved cabriole legs; turned stretchers; mellow ruddy patina. Massachusetts circa 1750-1760.
Purchased from Julie Rhodes, New Bedford, Massachusetts.
Ex-collection Israel Sack, Inc. 1939.
Ex-collection Charles K. Davis.
Illustrated ANTIQUES March 1941, page 128.

Ht. 45½″ Wd. 31½″ Dp. 30½″

The Davis Collection

P4333 Pilgrim maple child's slat back armchair; the posts with turned finials and the arms with mushroom terminals; the chair has a choice early aspect with the original dark brown or black paint showing the wear and character of the centuries. New England circa 1680-1700.
Ex-collection Charles K. Davis.

Ht. 26″ Wd. 15½″

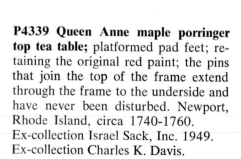

P4339 Queen Anne maple porringer top tea table; platformed pad feet; retaining the original red paint; the pins that join the top of the frame extend through the frame to the underside and have never been disturbed. Newport, Rhode Island, circa 1740-1760.
Ex-collection Israel Sack, Inc. 1949.
Ex-collection Charles K. Davis.

Ht. 26¼″ Lg. 33″ Dp. 26¼″

The Davis Collection

P4402 Sheraton gilt mirror with reeded columns, corinthian capitals and crosshatched frieze in black background; the landscaped eglomise panel is centered by a bold American eagle and stars in brilliant color on a white background. Salem, Massachusetts, circa 1800-1815.
Ex-collection Israel Sack, Inc. 1939.
Ex-collection Charles K. Davis.

Ht. 42¾″ Wd. 21½″

P4377 Hepplewhite mahogany and gilt mirror with original gilded urn and floral and wheat sprays; gilded side leaves; original eglomise glass panel in blue and gilt depicting a maritime scene. New York circa 1800-1810. A family record on the back reads "This glass brought by Stephen and Abigail Young, July 7, 1807, in New York. Brought on the stage. I. Parsippany and Stephen Young went there for it—Paid $18 for it."
Ex-collection Israel Sack, Inc. 1937.
Ex-collection Charles K. Davis.
Illustrated ANTIQUES March 1941, page 126.

Ht. 63″ Wd. 22¾″

The Davis Collection

P4335 Chippendale mahogany moulded leg wing chair; finely shaped serpentine wings and crest; original finish to base. Massachusetts circa 1760-1780.

This chair was part of the first purchase by Mr. Davis from Israel Sack, Inc., when he first entered our shop on May 20, 1936.

Ex-collection Israel Sack, Inc. 1936.
Ex-collection Charles K. Davis.
Illustrated ANTIQUES March 1941, page 128.

Ht. 46½″ Wd. 35″ Dp. 33½″

P4384 Classical gilt convex mirror; crested by finely sculptured eagle perched on a ball; a candle arm at each side with glass bobeches and prisms; original gilt. American or English circa 1810-1820.

Ht. 46½″ Wd. 29½″

The Davis Collection

P4400 Sheraton mahogany four post bed; slender and delicately turned and reeded foot posts superbly carved and of the quality of McIntire's handiwork; the urn with gothic panels; the inverted acanthus leaf capitals are joined by a flaring reeded collar and beaded borders; the birch foot posts are square tapered; arched pine headboard. Salem, Massachusetts, circa 1800-1810.
Ex-collection Israel Sack, Inc.
Ex-colection Charles K. Davis.

Ht. 6′10″ Lg. 6′6½″ Wd. 52″

Paul Revere the Patriot

P4403 Twelve engraved teaspoons made by Paul Revere with the cypher "JR" Boston, Massachusetts, circa 1788. Revere Account Book Volume II, page 71, dated 1788 lists 12 teaspoons made for Joseph Russell D[r].

Lg. 6⅜″

P4317 Bronze bust of Benjamin Franklin of important size and superb patina; supported on Sienna marble circular plinth with gadrooned base. French for the American market circa 1800-1810.

Ht. 14¼" Base 5¼" x 5¼"

P4318 Bronze bust of Benjamin Franklin; the brass gadrooned plinth is on a fluted Sienna marble column garlanded with brass laurel ring. French for the American market circa 1800-1810.

Ht. 10⅛" Base 3½" × 3½"

P4393 Chippendale mahogany serpentine ball and claw foot chest of drawers; a strong example with deep rich color retaining original willow brass handles and escutcheons. Massachusetts circa 1760-1780.

Ht. 33¾" Wd. 39" Dp. 21½"   1357

P4329 Silhouette of a minuteman titled "Elijah Taylor, Northampton (Mass.) 1780" signed F.C. 1780 in original gilt frame.

Ht. 14⅝″ Wd. 12¾″

P4311 Windsor bow back armchair of hickory and maple; bold knuckle arm terminals; bowed saddle seat; finely turned outsplayed legs; amber patina. Philadelphia circa 1760-1780.

Ht. 36¼″ Wd. 26″

P4321 Chippendale cherry chest-on-chest; broken arch top ending in bold carved rosettes and retaining the original urn shaped spiral finials; the piece is of slender proportions aided by quarter columns in top and bottom sections; the center drawer of the top row has a carved fan with dentilled border with a dentil moulding above; the ogee bracket feet are of distinctive design with a platformed base; the piece is in a superb state of preservation with a warm amber patina and retaining the original brasses. Connecticut circa 1760-1780.

Ht. 7'3" Wd. 38½" Dp. 19½"

A Philadelphia Masterpiece

P4303 Queen Anne walnut armchair of first rank; the chair features finely sculptured arms with knuckle terminals and lamb's tongue moulded arm supports; the webbed shell on the crest rail is complemented by shell carved knees; the cabriole legs are of superior grace and end in drake feet; the vase shaped splat is of solid finely figured crotch walnut; the seat frame and knee returns are the originals and the patina is a deep bronze. Philadelphia circa 1740-1760. A silvered placque at the back reads "Given by Anthony Franklin (his first wife's father) to Ezekiel Robins in 1795." An old photograph, dating about 1900 shows the chair in a parlor of the old homestead in Morristown, New Jersey.

Descent of the chair derived from family records is as follows:

1. Anthony Morris of Philadelphia, Brewer. Born 1705—died 1780; married 1730—Sarah Powel, daughter of Samuel Powel. (Anthony Morris was a wealthy landowner of Philadelphia. He lived in the brick Morris Mansion on North and Second Street.)

2. Deborah Morris, daughter of Anthony and Sarah (Powel) Morris. Born, Philadelphia 1736—died in New York 1787; married 1756 John Franklin, son of Thomas Franklin of New York.

3. Anthony Franklin, son of John and Deborah (Morris) Franklin. Born in New York 1768—died 1854.

3. Sarah Franklin, daughter of John and Deborah (Morris) Franklin. Born in New York 1757—died 1798; married Ezekiel Robins.

4. Direct descendant.

Ht. 42¼" Wd. 32½"

P4388 Pair Queen Anne maple scalloped front side chairs with slip seats; honey colored maple with some use of curly maple; excellently modelled cabriole legs and deep serpentine side contours give this pair a high rating. Massachusetts circa 1740-1760.

Ht. 40″

P4305 Hepplewhite mahogany shield back armchair; dark and light radiates form the inlaid motifs of the oval paterae of the splats and the crescent base; the crisply moulded arms are of beautiful serpentine contour; moulded tapered legs and arm supports; mint condition with mellow light brown patina. Salem, Massachusetts, circa 1780-1800.

Ht. 38¼″ Wd. 20″

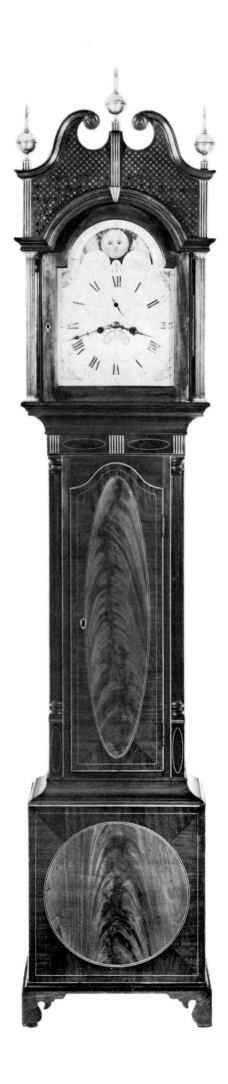

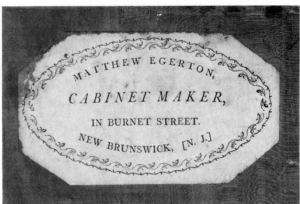

P4326 Hepplewhite mahogany tall clock bearing the original label of Matthew Egerton; the inlaid case is of typical New Jersey design; the distinctive punchwork of the scrollboard is contained in a gracefully arched pediment and flanked by inlaid pilasters; the enamelled dial is unsigned. Made by Matthew Egerton, Sr., New Brunswick, New Jersey, circa 1790-1800.

This clock was sold by Israel Sack to a Connecticut collector in 1938 and recently repurchased.

Ht. 7'9½" Wd. 19" Dp. 10"

P4304 Pair of Hepplewhite mahogany shield back side chairs; black and white radiates form the inlaid motifs of the oval paterae of the splats and crescent bases; moulded tapered legs; mellow light brown patina and fine condition. Salem, Massachusetts, circa 1780-1800.

Ht. 37½"

P4312 Classical mahogany octagonal top work table; one drawer with original lion brasses; the vase shaped column is bordered by carved diamond motifs in star punched background and centered by a framed mirror; the base platform has a ringed moulding and is supported by four outsplayed moulded legs with ring turned feet; beautiful golden color. Salem, Massachusetts, circa 1810-1820. A placque inside the drawer reads in part "Adams Table, Believed to have come from the Ladd Mansion, Portsmouth, New Hampshire—Mary Putnam Hart, Cambridge, Massachusetts, 1929."

Ht. 28½" Wd. 20¾" Dp. 15⅜"

P4397 Sheraton mahogany sofa; a gifted carver elevated the standard three panels of the crest into a master-piece of the carver's art; the carving is of a star punch or snowflake pattern in the manner of Salem carvers epitomized by the work of Samuel McIntire; the center panel features cornucopia roses and wheat while the end panels skillfully flowing vines and grapes; the carved rosettes and urn arm supports also have star punch background; turned legs with castered bulbous feet. The original patina is a rich bronze of great depth and mellowness. Salem, Massachusetts, circa 1800-1815.

Illustrated in Sack "One Hundred Important American Antiques" 1932, catalog No. 60.

Ht. 36½" Wd. 6'6" Dp. 25¼"

P4328 Rare wax bust of Stephen Decatur in full dress as Admiral of the Fleet (1779-1820) in brilliant condition with red collar and gilt epaulets; slight repair to nose; set in deep polished mahogany frame with brass ring; information from the seller (Sessler's Bookshop, Philadelphia) states it comes from the widow of Stanley Wilson, World I Marine Captain. She was a descendant of Washington Irving.

Ht. 8½″ Wd. 8⅜″ Dp. 1¾″

P4381 Queen Anne walnut desk; the case is supported on finely modelled platformed pad feet; stepped up interior, the top tier centered by fan carved door and pilastered document drawers; mellow light brown color; original brasses. Massachusetts circa 1750-1770.

Ht. 42″ Wd. 38¾″
Dp. 19½″ Wrtg. Lvl. 31″

P4358 Hepplewhite mahogany two drawer end table; the drawers bordered by an interrupted dart inlay repeated on cuffs of the line inlaid legs; the top with fan inlaid quadrants. Massachusetts cira 1780-1800.

Ht. 28⅞″ Wd. 17¾″ Dp. 15½″

P4399 Mahogany inlaid kidney shaped shelf clock made by Aaron Willard, Boston. The kidney shaped enamelled dial is inscribed "Aaron Willard, Boston"; bordered by gilded scrolled motifs; the hood has arrow and checkered inlaid stringing with diamond pierced fretwork crest and brass urn finials, ogee bracket feet, Aaron Willard, Boston, Massachusetts, circa 1810-1815.

Ht. 36¾″ Wd. 12½″ Dp. 6″

The General Schuyler Field Table

P4330 Pilgrim cherry or red gum folding trestle table; drop leaves of circular outline; the top is supported on pine block; the bold ball and ring turned supports are dovetailed to the block and mortised into the ogival shaped trestle shoe feet; the shoes are joined by a horizontal plank and the gates are simple vertical and horizontal slates; the leaves are fastened with the original butterfly hinges; the patina is the original with three centuries of maturity adding to its character and mellowness. New York circa 1670-1700. A more recent owner has scribed his initials and the date 1876 perhaps on the table's 200th birthday. A virtually identical example from Scotia, New York, is illustrated in "New York Furniture Before 1840" plate II.

According to family tradition this table was owned by General Philip Schuyler and was used by him as a field table during the Revolutionary Battle of Ticonderoga.

Illustrated ANTIQUES January 1934, pages 4 and 5.

Exhibited New York Furniture, Metropolitan Museum of Art 1934, catalogue # 9.

Ex-collection Mrs. Lauriston Walsh, Corning, New York.

Ex-collection Israel Sack, Inc. 1938.

Ht. 27¼″ Wd. 12¼″ closed—45″ open Lg. 35½″

P4396 Chippendale walnut flat top secretary; the raised panelled doors with cyma shaped crest are flanked by quarter columns in the corners; the desk interior features a concave arched center door with a small drawer with scooped arched fronts above each pigeonhole; ogee bracket feet; the moulding is attached to the base of the top section in typical Newport manner; the ogee feet are also of Newport outline; mellow light brown patina. Newport, Rhode Island, circa 1750-1770.

Ht. 6′9″ Wd. 36″ Dp. 19¾″ Writing Level 31⅛″

Two small Chippendale Serpentine Bureau

P4370 Chippendale mahogany serpentine front bureau with blocked ends, ogee bracket feet and bold overhanging top with moulded edge; finely figured mahogany with bronze patina. Massachusetts circa 1760-1780. A nearly matching companion to #4008 (illustrated here and previously described in Brochure 25, page 53).

Ht. 31¾" Wd. 37" Dp. 21½"

assachusetts Circa 1760-1780, close companions.

A JOHN SEYMOUR MASTERPIECE

P3235 Hepplewhite mahogany two drawer tambour desk of rare small size and superb proportions; the motifs display definitive characteristics to assign it to John Seymour's handiwork, namely the oval ivory drawer escutcheons and a similar escutcheon (concealed by the lid) to lock the tambours, the bellflower drops graduated in size, the modified spade feet, and the distinctive original pierced corner brackets; the bellflower inlaid panels repeating the inlay of the legs is a rare and effective variation; the drawers are bordered by a black and white chain inlay and retain the original oval brasses of beautifully chased design with spiral beaded bales; the tambour shutters are flanked by dark and light inlaid pilasters while the top is bordered by diagonal checkered inlay; a choice amber patina adds to the beauty of this little gem. Attributed to John Seymour and Son, Boston, Massachusetts, circa 1790-1805.

Ht. 41″ Wd. 33¾″ Dp. 20¼″

P4390 Three tiered revolving dumbwaiter; revolving dished discs with reeded cup turned shaft supported by tripod pedestal terminating in castered spade feet. This unusual American form has characteristic spade feet, a significant feature on Seymour pieces. Note the comparison to inlaid tambour desk on page 64 and inlaid card table illustrated brochure 28, page 22, labelled by John Seymour and Son, Boston, Massachusetts circa 1800-1810.

Ht. 46¼″ Diam. 24″ overall

P4325 Hepplewhite mahogany tall clock; the hood is superbly inlaid with intertwining vines and grapes flanked by panels of five petalled bellflower; the graceful swan's neck pediment is a beautiful fret design with an inlaid oriole perched on a branch fronting the plinth. To our knowledge the inlaid motif of a Baltimore oriole is unique. The waist and base have oval and square panels of mahogany in curly satinwood borders. Baltimore circa 1800-1815. A related clock by Charles Tinges, Baltimore, is in the Maryland Historical Society (see ANTIQUES May 1976, page 981).

Ht. 8′6½″ Wd. 20″ Dp. 10″

P4385 Chippendale mahogany claw and ball foot wing chair; the chair has the dynamic stance associated with this important Philadelphia form—the dramatically raking rear legs and compass shaped seat; the cabriole legs are boldly curved and retain a golden patina. Philadelphia circa 1760-1780.

Ht. 45¼″ Wd. 36″ Dp. 31¼″

P4322 Hepplewhite mahogany inlaid mirror with an inlaid eagle and 18 stars symbolizing the new Republic centering the crest; scrolled crest and base; original glass with carved and gilded and inlaid border; mellow brown color. New York circa 1810-1815.

Ht. 36¾″ Wd. 19¼″

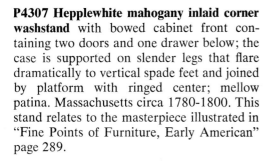

P4307 Hepplewhite mahogany inlaid corner washstand with bowed cabinet front containing two doors and one drawer below; the case is supported on slender legs that flare dramatically to vertical spade feet and joined by platform with ringed center; mellow patina. Massachusetts circa 1780-1800. This stand relates to the masterpiece illustrated in "Fine Points of Furniture, Early American" page 289.

Ht. 46″ Wd. 23″ Dp. 16″

P4324 Hepplewhite mahogany tall clock made and signed by Aaron Willard, Jr., Boston, Massachusetts, circa 1810-1820. The inside of the door retains the original printed directions established as engraved by Paul Revere (cf. Brigham "Paul Revere Engravings," plate 57); the case is beautifully proportioned; the door and base feature richly figured grain with crossbanded borders; the hood retains the original fretwork and finials; the circular dial features a bold rocking ship with lighthouse in background and is inscribed "Aaron Willard, Jr., Boston." Inside the case is branded the name H. N. Gardner, probably that of the owner.

Ht. 8′5″ Wd. 20″ Dp. 10″

P4398 Classical mahogany leaf carved pedestal work table bearing label of "J. Curtis, 153 Chamber Street, New York." This label illustrating the quality of some of Duncan Phyfe's contemporaries appears behind the lift up writing lid covered by the hinged top. The reeded outsplayed legs terminate in brass lion paw casters. This table is illustrated pl. 199 in "Duncan Phyfe and The English Regency" by Nancy McClelland.

Ht. 33″ Wd. 22¼″ Dp. 16″

P4302 Hepplewhite mahogany D-shaped sideboard with spade feet; a definitive choice example of John Seymour's handiwork; distinctive characteristics of the master are evidenced in the graduated bellflower drops, curly maple banded borders, oval ivory escutcheons, the corner brackets in the center arch, the side carrying handles and the superb selection of choice mahogany which retains a fine bronze patina. Attributed to John Seymour and Son, Boston, Massachusetts, circa 1790-1810. Illustrated "A Supplement to John and Thomas Seymour," by Vernon Stoneman, pages 46 and 47.

Ht. 40¼″ Lg. 5′8″ Dp. 26″

P4373 Banjo clock with diamond shaped dial; original eglomise glass panels in white background; the lower panel inscribed DANIEL MUNROE in octagon; the borders are powder blue and gilt; the borders of the base panel, waist panel, dial door and plinth are inlaid in a chain design with a reeded panel below the diamond door; the enamel dial is decorated with an American shield and scrolls in the corners; the entire hood slides forward to reveal the specially designed brass works; the brass bracket feet are to our knowledge unique and are apparently designed for the clock to be placed on a shelf. Made by Daniel Munroe, Concord, Massachusetts, circa 1810-1830. A diamond model clock by Munroe is in Sturbridge and one by Jabez Baldwin is in Winterthur. See Montgomery, Federal Furniture, pl. #161.

Ht. 38¾″ Wd. 11″ Dp. 4″

P4316 Bronze bust of George Washington in uniform on brass plinth and base; green mottled marble plinth. French for the American market circa 1800-1810.

Ht. 11⅞″
Base 3⅝″ square

P4314 Terra cotta medallion depicting Franklin in a fur cap and imprinted "B. Franklin, American"; in attractive fruitwood frame. French for the American market circa 1800.

9½″ x 9⅜″ including frame

MINIATURE

P4310 Hepplewhite mahogany inlaid miniature chest of two drawers; the line inlaid drawers are flanked by diagonal inlaid pilasters with intersecting vine branches above; the top has fan inlaid quadrants in the corners; the case is supported on tapered inlaid legs. Connecticut circa 1780-1800.

Ht. 10⅞″ Wd. 16⅝″ Dp. 8⅛″

P4391 Sheraton mahogany and branch satinwood bowed shaped card table; a rich mellow color and excellence of detailing place this in a high level of desirability. Boston or Salem, Massachusetts, circa 1810.

Ht. 29½″ Wd. 35¾″
Dp. 17½″ closed 35″ open

MINIATURE

P4309 Chippendale mahogany miniature cabinet; finely modelled ogee bracket feet; the twin panelled doors with moulded borders conceal an interior of three long narrow drawers with chestnut linings (two drawers missing); the original side carrying handles; fine bronze patina. Rhode Island circa 1750-1780.

Ht. 13½″ Wd. 16⅜″ Dp. 11⅜″

P4386 Chippendale mahogany blockfront bureau; bold round blocking; bracket feet; the mahogany is the dense San Domingan variety; bronze patina. Massachusetts circa 1750-1770.

Ht. 30″ Wd. 36″ Dp. 21⅛″

P4387 Chippendale walnut dish top bird cage candlestand; one piece top with fine swirling grain; the column bulbous and ring turned; cabriole legs with platformed pad feet; old or original finish. Philadelphia circa 1750-1770.

Ht. 29¼″ Diameter 23½″

P4369 Mahogany barometer; pedimented crest; octagonal panelled base; finely figured crotch mahogany; brass engraved index plate inscribed "Jm Francis, 13 Dock St., Philadelphia." The barometer retains the original iron L shaped wall backet proving its use as a household rather than a ship barometer. Philadelphia circa 1810-1830.

Ht. 39″ Wd. 5″ Dp. 3″

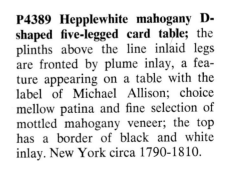

P4378 Chippendale mahogany tripod tip candlestand of intermediate size; the top serpentine; urn shaped column; finely modelled cabriole legs with platformed pad feet; the contemporary brand J. P. DAVIS on the underside of the top is either the original owner or maker. Massachusetts circa 1760-1780.

Ht. 28½″ Top 21¼″ x 21″

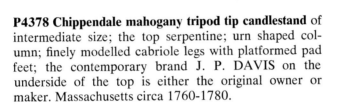

P4389 Hepplewhite mahogany D-shaped five-legged card table; the plinths above the line inlaid legs are fronted by plume inlay, a feature appearing on a table with the label of Michael Allison; choice mellow patina and fine selection of mottled mahogany veneer; the top has a border of black and white inlay. New York circa 1790-1810.

Ht. 29¼″ Wd. 36″ Dp. 18″

P4357 Sheraton mahogany serpentine shaped card table with turret ends; the front, sides and turrets with superbly figured crotch satinwood veneer; the front centered by rectangular cross-banded panel; finely modelled bulbous reeded legs; inlaid top border; the flaming figure of the mahogany matches the flame of the satinwood and both are enhanced by a superb mellow brown patina. Boston, Massachusetts, circa 1800-1810.

Ex-collection Andrew Varick Stout, pioneer collector.

Illustrated Girl Scout Loan Exhibition, catalogue #693, 1929.

Ht. 29¾″ Wd. 37″ Dp. 18¼″

P4394 Hepplewhite mahogany pembroke table; oval shaped top and case; a drawer in one end with oval bordered panel; the tapered legs are inlaid on two sides with shaded bellflower drops connected by loops with oval panels of satinwood on the plinths above; old or original finish. New York circa 1780-1800.

Ht. 28½″ Lg. 31″ Wd. Closed 20½″—Open 40″

P4382 Pair of Hepplewhite mahogany shield back side chairs; the four bowed slats emanate from a fan carved crescent, each slat with thumbnail and beaded carving with reeding above; the tapered legs have bellflower inlay on the front, reeded sides and end in spade feet; fine condition and bronze color. New York circa 1790-1800.
Ex-collection Andrew Varick Stout, pioneer collector.

Ht. 38½″

P4320 Bronze bust of General George Washington in uniform on marble base; the plinth is inscribed "First in War, First in Peace and First in the hearts of his Countrymen." This is the inscription that appears on bronze Washington busts for the American market but is rare in this form. French for the American market circa 1800-1810.

Ht. 8¼″ Wd. 3⅞″ Dp. 2⅔″

Chippendale mahogany tall clock by Jacob Godshalk, Towamencin, Pennsylvania, circa 1760-1770. Illustrated ANTIQUES December 1946, page 304. Illustrated "American Antiques from Israel Sack Collection" Vol. V, pages 116 and 1165. Private collection.

Mahogany "grandmother" or half high clock by Joshua Wilder, Hingham, Massachusetts, circa 1821. Illustrated "American Antiques from Israel Sack Collection" Vol. IV, page 1095. Private collection.

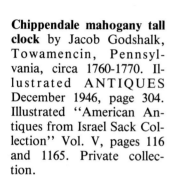

Bridal lighthouse clock by Simon Willard, Roxbury, Massachusetts, circa 1820-1830. Illustrated "Living With Antiques" Alice Winchester, page 95. Illustrated "American Antiques from Israel Sack Collection" Vol. V, page 1268. Private collection.

Mahogany shelf clock by Simon Willard, Boston, Massachusetts, circa 1770-1780. Illustrated "Living With Antiques" Alice Winchester, page 94. Private collection.

continued on page 1389

THE TARADASH COLLECTION
(Continued)

Classical mahogany settee, attributed to Duncan Phyfe, New York circa 1810-1820. Art Institute of Chicago.

Set of 6 Hepplewhite mahogany side chairs, Connecticut circa 1780-1800. Illustrated "Living With Antiques" Alice Winchester, page 92. Illustrated "American Antiques from Israel Sack Collection" Vol. III, page 827. Israel Sack, Inc.

Hepplewhite oval decorated side chair, made for Elias Haskett Derby, Salem, Massachusetts, circa 1790-1800. Private collection.

Pair of Classical mahogany harp back side chairs, attributed to Duncan Phyfe, New York circa 1810-1820. Illustrated ANTIQUES January 1953, page 44. Illustrated "American Antiques from Israel Sack Collection" Vol. IV, page 1104. Private collection.

continued on page 1390

Classical mahogany accordian dining table, Philadelphia circa 1810-1820. Illustrated "Living With Antiques" Alice Winchester, page 92. Illustrated "American Antiques from Israel Sack Collection" Vol. V, pages 1306 and 1307. Private collection.

Hepplewhite mahogany inlaid pembroke table, Baltimore, Maryland, circa 1780-1800. Illustrated "American Antiques from Israel Sack Collection" Vol. VI, page 1685. Private collection

Banjo clock with New York State coat of arms by Elnathan Taber, Boston, Massachusetts, dated 1804. Illustrated "American Antiques from Israel Sack Collection" Vol. VI, page 1574. Illustrated "Living With Antiques" Alice Winchester, page 92. Israel Sack, Inc.

Sheraton Martha Washington or lolling chair, Portsmouth, New Hampshire, circa 1800-1815. Illustrated "American Antiques from Israel Sack Collection" Vol. V, page 1287. Americana collection, Department of State.

. . . . and a great collection has passed to another generation of collectors.

INDEX

By Donald R. Sack, Israel Sack, Inc., New York

This index has been arranged in five ways:

First: Form: Items listed alphabetically and also listed in period. Example: Chairs — Pilgrim, William & Mary, etc.

Second: Regional: Items listed by location. Example: New York: Bureaus, Chairs, etc. Also large states such as Massachusetts have centers within them listed separately.

Third: Cabinetmakers: Listed in alphabetical order.

Fourth: Clockmakers: Listed in alphabetical order.

Fifth: Silversmiths and Painters: Listed in alphabetical order.

Each item is listed by p for page number and item number following the page number in the catalog. Example: p. 100, *68*.

Also in the index, where the craftsman is known, the name is preceded by page number and item number.

FORM

REGIONAL